Computer
Applications
and Algorithms

Computer Applications and Algorithms

C. William Gear

UNIVERSITY OF ILLINOIS
Urbana, Illinois

SCIENCE RESEARCH ASSOCIATES, INC.
Chicago, Henley-on-Thames, Sydney, Toronto

A Subsidiary of IBM

Acquisition Editor: John Levstik
Development Editor: Richard Myers
Project Management: Newcomer/Muncil Associates
Design: R. David Newcomer
Cover: Arv Tessing
Composition: G & S Typesetters, Inc.

Library of Congress Cataloging-in-Publication Data

Gear, C. William (Charles William), 1935–
    Computer applications and algorithms.

    "Revision of the Applications and algorithms
modules from the Introduction to computers, structured
programming, and applications series"—Pref.
    Includes index.
    1. Electronic digital computers—Programming.
2. Algorithms.   3. FORTRAN (Computer program language)
4. PASCAL (Computer program language)   I. Title.
QA76.6.G375   1986   005.1′2   85-22058
ISBN 0-574-21970-6

Printed in the United States of America

10   9   8   7   6   5   4   3   2   1

Contents

Preface

The objective of this book is to teach the topic of problem solving by computer by examining the development of a number of important methods in several application areas.

This book is a revision of the *Applications* and *Algorithms* modules from the *Introduction to Computers, Structured Programming, and Applications* series. It can be used independently for a problem-solving course or a second programming course, or with a programming language book for a two-semester introductory course.

Programs in this book are written in an informal language, whose structures are those found in common languages. Transliteration into an available language should therefore be straightforward. Since the programs are not intended for direct computer implementation, display (i.e., indentation) is used to indicate the extent of control structures, without reference to rules concerning semicolons, etc., which vary from language to language. Also, for redundancy and hence easier comprehension by the student, all structures are terminated with an appropriate **end** statement, such as **endif**. The temptation in using an informal language is to give it a formal definition, thereby forcing the student to learn yet another language, one that is relatively useless because it is not accepted by any machine. I have therefore tried to avoid ambiguity by limiting use of program and data structures to those that are common to most languages. For the majority of problems studied at this stage in a student's career, it is not necessary to use complex structures whose implementation differs from language to language. For those problems that demand complex structures, I have tried to give informal descriptions and to avoid language-specific features. For similar reasons, variables are not declared in program fragments unless some sort of declaration is essential to comprehension. This is not to suggest that students should not declare variables if they are using a compiler that does not enforce declaration. Indeed, some compilers for languages that do not require declarations, such as FORTRAN, provide compile options that cause undeclared variables to be flagged. If those options are available, I recommend that they be used.

The author and publisher acknowledge with gratitude the comments of Dr. James A. Gentiles, University of Pittsburgh at Johnstown, Joe Lambert, Pennsylvania State University, and Dieter Schmidt, University of Cincinnati, who read the manuscript and offered many useful suggestions.

Introduction: Algorithms and Problem Solving

In this book we are concerned with the solution of problems by computer. One very dull way of learning how to solve problems is to be force-fed a set of methods that it is hoped will be sufficient for all the problems encountered. Even if this approach were feasible, there would be little point in learning the methods, because each could be encoded in a subprogram and made available in a program library. Indeed, if we have a problem that is exactly of the type handled by a standard library subprogram or package, we should use that library code and not waste our time reinventing the wheel. Unfortunately (or fortunately for our intellectual stimulation), not all problems we encounter in our lives fit the mold of existing codes, so we must be prepared to develop ways to solve new problems.

In using computers we are not usually concerned with the solution of a single specific problem—that is, one whose data is given and for which there is a single answer; rather, we are concerned with developing methods and writing programs that will give the answers to a range of similar problems once their data is specified. For example, if we were asked to compute the compound interest for three years on \$1,000 at 10%, we would not normally write a program to do it; we would probably use a hand calculator (or a microcomputer or interactive computer terminal in a calculator mode) to get the answer directly. Indeed, for this problem most of us would mentally calculate the answer of \$331. We might, however, write a program if we were asked to be prepared to calculate the compound interest for N years on C dollars at P percent interest per year (unless we had a calculator with such a function built into it, which is equivalent to using a library code to solve the problem); and we would almost certainly write a program to handle a more complicated problem of this type (for example, calculation of the repayment schedule for a mortgage)—again, unless there was a library code available to handle the problem for us. Therefore, when we talk about problem solving we do not mean the solution of a single specific problem; rather, we mean the development of a method (algorithm) and/or program to solve instances of the problem for which specific data is given. There are situations in which a computer may be needed to solve a single problem because of its complexity, but in such cases the considerations will be very similar to those that arise in the development of a program.

There are a number of books on problem solving* that, on the surface, are concerned with the solution of particular problems. Their real concern, however, is with the development of techniques for solving classes of similar problems (and particularly with the ways in which people solve problems). They are good background reading for developing problem-solving skills that can be important in solving computer problems—that is, in developing programs. Frequently we can understand more about the process needed to solve a problem if we examine a particular instance of it, for it is clearly true that if we cannot solve a particular instance, even with the aid of a computer, we have no hope of writing a program to solve a class of similar problems. However, we must not forget that there may be cases that do not arise in the particular instance we are looking at but must nevertheless be covered in the general program.

It is tempting to think that we could develop a general methodology that would lead us to a solution for any problem that might arise. Despite the hopes of a number of early philosophers and mathematicians, however (see Polya, 1962, for a brief discussion of this), such a universal technique was later shown not to exist (although artificial intelligence researchers are trying to develop methods that will work in limited contexts). Therefore, fortunately or unfortunately, the computer cannot be used to replace the programmer completely, and we must learn how to develop solution methods.

In order to learn how to write programs to solve classes of problems, we

---

*For example, Duncker (1945), Polya (1954a, 1954b, 1957, 1962, 1965), and Wickelgren (1974).

must acquire a number of skills. We must be able to recognize problems, or parts of problems, for which well-known methods exist and we must know how to find code that may already have been written to handle such problems. We must learn how to break a large problem down into simpler subproblems that have been solved before, or for which we can find a method of solution. We must also be able to recognize when it is possible to solve a new problem by modifying an existing method for a similar problem. Thus, part of the material we need to learn is a set of methods for common problems and an understanding of when to use them. In this book we will look at a number of important methods, and part of our objective is to learn how they can be applied. However, we also want to know how these methods work, so we can understand how to adapt them to similar problems. More importantly, we want to develop our problem-solving skills so that we can design methods for solving various problems. The best way to do this is to combine the study of the development of existing methods with practice in solving similar problems.

Although there is no universal method, there are a number of standard techniques that can be used for many problems. In this first chapter we will demonstrate these common techniques on a number of extremely simple problems, in preparation for the study of more complex examples later in the book. In each case, we will try to understand how the method could have been developed for the first time and how it could be modified and applied to similar problems. At the end of this chapter we will discuss the general philosophy of problem solving, based on our initial examples.

1.1   SOME SIMPLE EXAMPLES

In this section we will examine some extremely simple examples, in order to illustrate methods of solution without obscuring the main points with tedious details of a particular problem.

Example 1.1
Interest Computation

We start with the example mentioned earlier and some extensions of it. Suppose we want to calculate the compound interest for N years on C dollars of capital at P percent interest per year. A direct approach is to follow the sequence of steps that would be executed by bankers who loaned this money. They would first record the amount of the initial capital, C, as the loan amount owed, L. At the end of the first year they would compute the interest on the loan amount, $L*P/100$, and add it to the amount owed, L. At the end of the second year they would repeat this process, and so on for N years. Finally, the bankers would find the interest as the difference between the amount owed, L, and the original capital, C. We could use a program with a loop in the form

```
Loan ← Capital
do for Year ← 1 to N
    Loan ← Loan + Loan*Percent/100.
    enddo
Interest ← Loan − Capital
```

Note that we have used identifiers of several characters (Loan, Capital, etc.) because they give more meaning to variable names than the single letters conventionally used in mathematics. Also we have mixed upper- and lowercase letters in identifiers for readability in this example. Generally we prefer to do this, especially if the language we are using accepts both kinds of letters. We have to be careful, however, because some systems distinguish between upper- and lowercase, and the identifiers Loan, LOAN, and loan would therefore represent different objects in these systems. Other systems do not distinguish upper- and lowercase, so these identifiers would all reference the same object from the same point in the program. To avoid these potentially confusing problems and to set off the names of identifiers from the surrounding text as much as possible, we will use uppercase letters in identifiers in the majority of examples in this book. They are set in a typeface different from that of the regular text, as in PERCENT. In writing mathematical expressions we will usually revert to the conventions of mathematics, using italic single letters for variables unless the context demands otherwise.

To return to our first example, many readers may have already noticed that the method we chose is not a good one for several reasons. For example, the assignment statement inside the loop could be simplified to

```
LOAN ← LOAN*(1. + PERCENT/100.)
```

(For that matter, the expression $(1 + P/100)$, whose value does not change inside the loop, could be calculated before the start of the loop. However, this is an optimization that is done by some compilers and is not a factor we should be concerned with in the design stage of a computer method.) We also notice that the loop simply multiplies LOAN by the factor $(1 + P/100)$ a total of N times, so that we are calculating $(1 + P/100)^N C$ as the value of LOAN. Hence, the calculation could be performed with the single statement

```
INTEREST ← ((1. + PERCENT/100.)**N − 1.)*CAPITAL
```

where the exponentiation operator is designated by **. The lessons we can learn from this example are that sometimes a *direct calculation* can be used to get the answer to a problem (this frequently happens when the calculation is "simulating" a straightforward action that may happen in real life) but that this method can often be improved with a small amount of mathematical analysis.

Let us extend this example a little, by asking how much a depositor would have in the bank if C dollars of capital were invested every year for N years at P percent interest. Before rushing into the solution, let us make sure we have the facts straight: at the beginning of the first year, C dollars will be put in the bank. At the end of the first year, a fraction $P/100$ of whatever is in the account will be added to it. The following morning, the depositor will add another C to the account. We want to stop after N years—that is, after the Nth interest payment has been credited but before the next C dollars have been added at the start of the $N + $ 1st year. This detail may seem trivial, but in the initial loose statement of the problem it was not clear whether we were to include the next year's payment. *In many problem statements a lot of "facts" are left unstated, and in some cases different readers may make different assumptions. Before the problem can be solved, we must understand what data we are starting with.*

We could develop a program to solve this problem using the previous approach—that is, we could simulate the steps undertaken by the bank and the depositor. A modification of the earlier program could be used; its first statement would be replaced by

```
BALANCE ← 0
```

where we are using the variable `BALANCE` instead of `LOAN` for its better mnemonic value. This simulates opening the account with nothing in it. The first statement inside the loop would then be replaced by two statements:

```
BALANCE ← BALANCE + CAPITAL
BALANCE ← BALANCE*(1. + PERCENT/100.)
```

The first of these simulates the deposit of the `CAPITAL`, C, by the investor at the beginning of the year, and the second simulates the addition of the interest at the end of the year. If we actually wanted to know the balance during the year or at the end of each year, this would be the most straightforward approach; `BALANCE` could be printed immediately before or after the interest calculation, respectively. If we need only the balance at the end of the year, the two statements could be combined into the single statement

```
BALANCE ← (BALANCE + CAPITAL)*(1. + PERCENT/100.)
```

If we only need to know the answer at the end of N years, we could do the mathematical analysis so as to avoid execution of the program loop. A general way to do this analysis is to write down the mathematical form of the values of all variables changed in the loop after each pass through the loop and then attempt to find a simple form for these expressions. In this example we see that after the first pass through the loop we get

$$B = C(1 + P/100)$$

where B is the value of the variable BALANCE. After the second pass we see that we will get

$$\begin{aligned} B &= (C(1 + P/100) + C)(1 + P/100) \\ &= C((1 + P/100)^2 + (1 + P/100)) \end{aligned}$$

and so on. However, in many cases we can find the answer faster by thinking about the problem differently and using the results of earlier work. (Returning to "first principles" is often a way to get to an answer, but it is better to build on previous experience.) In the first form of this example, we saw that an initial investment of C grew to $(1 + P/100)^N C$ in N years. Thus, the first C that is invested will have grown by that much in the investment period. The next C added to the account is there for only $N - 1$ years, so it grows only to $(1 + P/100)^{N-1} C$, and so on, until the last C invested grows only to $(1 + P/100)C$. Thus the result is

$$S = (1 + P/100)C + (1 + P/100)^2 C + \cdots + (1 + P/100)^N C \quad (1.1)$$

Many of you will recognize this as the sum of a geometric series *

---

*A geometric series is one in which each term is a constant multiple of the preceding term. Such series occur frequently in scientific and commercial calculations. Finding the sum of these and other series is a common problem in calculations, and the ability to sum some series is thus an important mathematical skill for scientists. Such series can be summed on a computer by simply adding all the terms, but this method may lead to inaccuracies if a large number of terms are involved and is inefficient in its use of computer time. Like program development, summing series is a skill that improves with practice and exposure to standard methods. Many series of this sort can be summed by finding a way to write down a similar sum and then forming some arithmetic combination of the two versions that is simpler than the original form. In this case, we form rS, where S is given by (1.2), to get

$$rS = ra + r^2 a + r^3 a + \cdots + r^N a$$

We note that this is very much like (1.2); it does not have the first term, a, but has an additional term, $r^N a$. By subtracting (1.2) from the last equation we get $(r - 1)S = (r^N - 1)a$, from which the result, equation (1.3), follows.

Computer Applications and Algorithms

$$S = a + ra + r^2a + \cdots + r^{N-1}a \tag{1.2}$$

where $a = (1 + P/100)C$ and $r = (1 + P/100)$. The sum (1.2) is

$$S = a\frac{r^N - 1}{r - 1} \tag{1.3}$$

so the calculation represented by (1.1) can be performed by

```
BALANCE ← CAPITAL*(100./PERCENT + 1.)*
  ((1. + PERCENT/100.)**N - 1.)
```

In this example we see again that direct calculation can be used, but that a small amount of mathematical analysis can yield a better program. However, the analysis is more complex in this case and could take longer if the programmer did not recognize the sum involved or see a way to sum the series immediately. If the answer to only one such problem is required, it is almost certainly better to use the longer but more straightforward code than it is to spend a large amount of time doing the analysis. Computer time is relatively inexpensive compared to people time, so the gains are worthwhile only if the program is to be executed many times (the analysis still has to be done only once) or if the additional accuracy makes the analysis time worthwhile. In this example, negligible additional accuracy is obtained because of the nature of the series.

In fact, the summed form in this case is actually less accurate if we follow business practices that were neglected when we stated the problem. We have been doing the calculation to machine accuracy, presumably in floating-point arithmetic, so that quantities such as `PERCENT/100.` can be represented. When banks make interest calculations, they use rules for rounding the amount of each calculation to cents, or possibly to mils, where a mil is $0.001. These rules should be reflected in our calculations. They can be handled by carrying the amount as an integer number of cents or mils, as appropriate, calculating the interest at the end of each year as a floating-point number, and rounding back to an integer again after each year. This calculation requires the use of a program loop.

Example 1.2
Search in a List of Data

A common computer task is the location of a particular item in a list of items, given part of the information; for example, the location of a telephone number, given the name of the person in a list of *records*, each record containing a name, address, and telephone number. The part of the information used to locate the record desired, in this case the name, is called the *key*. If we assume that the list is unsorted (that is, the names appear in no particular order), the only way to find whether a particular name is on the list is to look at every record. This may be done by starting at the first record and examining each one in turn until either the name is found or the last record has been examined. This process is called a *sequential search*. It is slow because we are checking every case, but in this example we have no choice, since without further information on the organization of the data this is our only way of determining whether an entry is not present. The method is an example of an *enumeration* method, in which we count (enumerate) our way through all the cases. If the nature of the problem is to find out which of a known set of cases gives the answer, an enumeration method is always a possible approach, although it is likely to be slower than other methods, if they exist.

Example 1.3
Greatest Common Divisor

The greatest common divisor (GCD) of two positive integers M and N is the largest integer that divides M and N exactly. The problem of finding the GCD is not particularly important, but it is a good example for method development. Since the GCD is at least 1 and is no larger than the smaller of M and N—that is, $\min(M, N)$—we can clearly use an enumeration method by counting back from $\min(M, N)$ to 1 until we find the first integer that divides M and N exactly. For large integers this could be very slow, so we try to use a little common sense. To simplify the discussion, let us assume that $M \leq N$. (We can swap the values if this is not true.) If M divides N, then the answer is M and we are done. If not, we do not want to use enumeration, because a large value of M could lead to a long execution time. Therefore, let us try to reduce the size of the numbers involved. If G is the GCD of M and N, then G clearly divides $N - M, N - 2M, N - 3M, \ldots$, and $N - qM$ exactly, where q is the integer quotient of N divided by M. The last of these numbers is the remainder of N divided by M, say R, and lies between zero and $M - 1$. If this remainder is zero, M divides N, a case we have already handled. Therefore, we have only to deal with the case of a nonzero remainder. It is easy to see that the GCD of R and M is also the GCD of M and N. (We have already seen that G divides R. Hence the GCD of R and M is at least G. Since the GCD of R and M divides $N = R + qM$, it must be no larger than G. Hence it is G.) We have therefore reduced the problem to that of finding the GCD of R and M. We could now use enumeration, but having found a good thing we may as well continue. We can repeat the process, with M and N replaced by R and M. If R divides M we have the answer; if not, we get a new remainder. Since the numbers get smaller each time and we are working with integers, we will eventually get a remainder of zero, at which time the last divisor will be the GCD. The method is shown in Program 1-1. The **loop-endloop** pair of statements causes

■ **Program 1.1   Greatest common divisor**

```
LEAST ← Min(M,N)
MOST ← Max(M,N)
loop
    REMAINDER ← remainder of MOST divided by LEAST
    if REMAINDER = 0
        then GCD ← LEAST
            exit loop
        else MOST ← LEAST
            LEAST ← REMAINDER
        endif
endloop
```

indefinite execution of the enclosed statements—that is, until some other statement terminates execution. The **exit loop** statement immediately terminates execution of the current loop.

Two points are illustrated by this example: (1) although enumeration provides a method for solving problems with only a finite number of possible answers, other methods are usually faster, and (2) we can often find a way of solving a problem by reducing it to a simpler problem; in this case we reduced the problem to a set of smaller values.

Example 1.4
Square Root

The problem is to compute an approximation to $\sqrt{a}$. (We cannot compute the exact value in general, because the square root of a number may not be representable to machine accuracy.) Suppose we have an approximation to $\sqrt{a}$, say x_0. We then expect a/x_0 also to be an approximation to $\sqrt{a}$, and to be smaller than $\sqrt{a}$ if x_0 is larger than $\sqrt{a}$ and vice versa. This suggests that we try taking the average of these two values as a new approximation, say x_1, and repeating this process a number of times using

$$x_{n+1} = (x_n + a/x_n)/2$$

This is the Newton method for finding $\sqrt{a}$, named after the English mathematician Isaac Newton. It can be shown that if $a \geq 0$ and $x_0 > 0$, then $x_1 \geq x_2 \geq \cdots \geq \sqrt{a}$, with equality holding only if $x_0 = \sqrt{a}$. This is an *iterative method*. The successive approximations, x_n, are called the *iterates*. In an iterative method we compute a new approximation in terms of a previous approximation. The new approximation should be, in some sense, a better approximation than the old one. In this case the new approximation is closer to the solution than the older one, and it can be shown that it gets closer to the true solution very rapidly. Iterative methods are sometimes called trial and error methods, because the next iterate depends in some way on the amount by which the previous iterate differs from the solution.

For an iterative method to be of value, it must be possible to show that the answers eventually become more accurate. We must also have a way of stopping the iteration, because in most cases the iterate will never reach the correct answer. In this particular example we can stop when the iterates stop decreasing, because, to machine accuracy, we will fairly quickly reach the point at which there are no more representable values between x_n and $\sqrt{a}$. Unfortunately, it is not easy to find such simple stopping criteria in some problems. That a sequence is decreasing toward an answer does not mean that it will get close to the answer. For example, the sequence 1.0, 0.9, 0.89, 0.889, 0.8889, 0.88889, . . . keeps decreasing and is always larger than zero. However, it does not approach zero; its limit is $0.888 \cdots = 8/9$.

Example 1.5
Bisection

In the previous example we were, in effect, trying to solve the nonlinear equation $f(x) = x^2 - a = 0$. Here, $f(x)$ is a *function* in the mathematical sense. As in a computer language, x is the *argument* of the function f. In this example we are trying to find a value of the argument that makes the corresponding value of the function zero. Let us consider the case $0 < a < 1$. We note that $f(0) < 0$ and $f(1) > 0$. Looking at Figure 1-1, we see that the graph of $f(x)$ must cross the x-axis somewhere between 0 and 1. Mathematically, we are requiring that $f(x)$ be *continuous*, that $f(0) < 0$, and that $f(1) > 0$. This is sufficient to ensure that

FIGURE 1-1 x^2-a

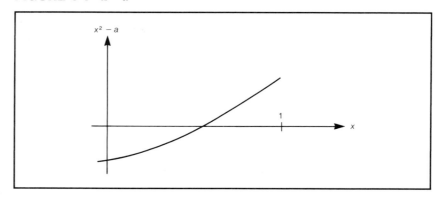

FIGURE 1-2 Relation of computed points to solution

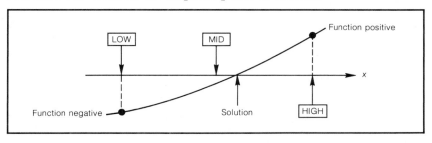

FIGURE 1-3 Moving LOW to MID

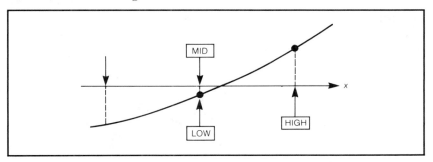

there is a value of x, say $\hat{x}$, between 0 and 1 such that $f(\hat{x}) = 0$. We say that $\hat{x}$ is a *zero* of $f(x)$ or a *root* of the equation $f(x) = 0$.

In the GCD example we saw that the approach of trying to make the problem smaller was a helpful one, so let us try it again here. We know that there is a solution between 0 and 1; it would be nice to narrow down that interval. Therefore, let us divide the interval in two by selecting the midpoint of the interval (0.5) and considering the two half-size intervals (0, 0.5) and (0.5, 1). The value at the middle point must be either positive or negative (taking zero to be either positive or negative; it does not matter which). From this information we can determine which of the two half-size intervals must contain a zero. Let us use the variable names LOW and HIGH for the left and right ends (0 and 1 in this example) of the interval that we know to contain a solution. In Figure 1-2 we illustrate the case in which $f(\text{MID})$ is negative, where MID is the midpoint of the interval (LOW, HIGH). In this case there will be a zero between MID and HIGH. Consequently we can move the left end of the interval, LOW, to the position of MID, as shown in Figure 1-3, thus halving the length of the interval. Similarly, if $f(\text{MID})$ is positive, then the left half of the interval is guaranteed to contain a zero. In this case, we can move HIGH to the position of MID. In either case, we can halve the length of the interval known

FIGURE 1-4 Moving HIGH to MID

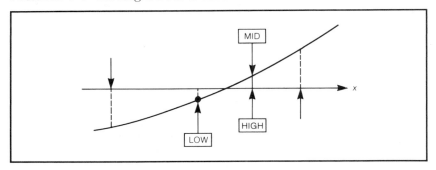

FIGURE 1-5 Successive approximations

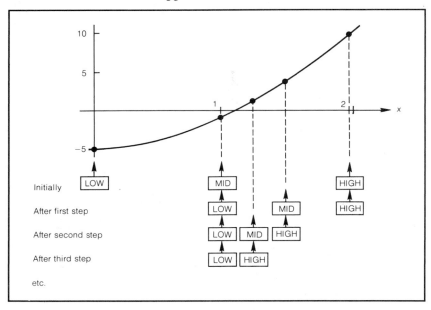

to contain a zero. The same process can be repeated to keep reducing the size of the interval known to contain a zero. In Figure 1-4 we illustrate the second step of the process, in which HIGH is moved to the position of MID. In Figure 1-5 we illustrate several steps in the process.

Unless we happen to land on a value MID for which $f(\text{MID})$ is exactly zero, we will never find a zero by this process, but we will reduce the length of the interval at every step, so our uncertainty as to the value of the zero will decrease. Since we cannot, in general, expect to find an exact solution to a problem such as a square root, we can stop when we have enough accuracy to satisfy our needs. By choosing the midpoint of the

■ Program 1.2   Method of bisection

```
BISECTION: program
```
> *Program to solve the equation F(X) = 0 by the method of bisection.*
> *F(X) is assumed to be negative when X = 0 and positive when X = 1.*
```
    real LOW,HIGH,MID,X,F
    LOW ← 0
    HIGH ← 1
    do while (HIGH − LOW) > 0.002
        MID ← (LOW + HIGH)/2.0
        F ← value of F for argument MID
        if F < 0
            then LOW ← MID
            else HIGH ← MID
            endif
        enddo
    X ← (LOW + HIGH)/2.0
```
> *Solution is X.*
```
endprogram
```

remaining interval as an approximation to the solution, we reduce the uncertainty to just half the interval length. For example, if we wanted to know the solution to within 0.001, we could stop when the interval did not exceed 0.002, as shown in Program 1-2. In this program we have indicated that the variables involved should be reals, because the program could fail if they were integers. (Why?) Comments are printed in italics, a practice we will generally follow in programs. English statements in the typeface used for programs are to be interpreted as informal program statements, which in an actual program should be replaced by appropriate code.

Example 1.6
Binary Search

In Example 1.2 we observed that the only way to search in an unordered list was to look at each entry until a matching entry was found or all examples had been checked. However, suppose the list is ordered. In this case we can use other searching techniques that take advantage of the ordering and will be much faster. If you think about the way you look up an entry in, say, a dictionary, you will probably think of some ways to solve this problem. (This would be another example of finding a way to program a problem by imitating, or *simulating*, what we would do by hand.)

In this example we could also apply the experience we gained from the previous example. Suppose that the list contains alphabetical names and that its entries are numbered 1, 2, 3, . . . , N. We can think of the list

FIGURE 1-6 Sorted list viewed as a function graph

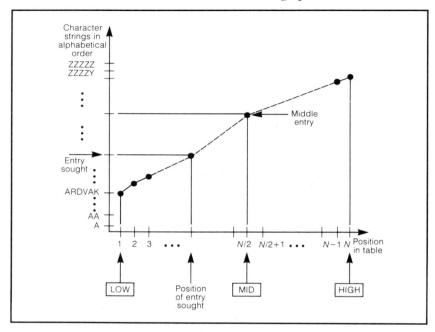

items as specifying a function that associates the integers 1 through N with alphabetical names, as shown in Figure 1-6. The figure has the entry numbers along the horizontal axis and "all possible" combinations of letters along the vertical axis (or at least all possible combinations up to the maximum length of names we will deal with). Some of these combinations are entries in the list, so each entry in the list is represented by a single point. For example, if the fifth list entry is ALPHA, the point (5, ALPHA) would be in the graph of the function. The graph of the function is really a set of isolated points representing the entries in the list, but we have drawn a line connecting the entries to emphasize the similarities with the previous example. Since the list is sorted, the graph is always increasing as we move to the right. (Mathematically, this is called a *monotonically increasing* function.) When we search in the list, we are specifying a value on the vertical axis for which we want to find the corresponding entry in the list—that is, the number on the horizontal axis. From this figure we can see that the problem is similar to that of finding where the function crosses the horizontal line corresponding to the entry we want to locate. This immediately suggests that we use a method similar to that of the previous example and first try the middle point, labeled MID in the figure.

Here the similarity with the previous example ends. In the previous example we were guaranteed a solution because we had a continuous function: there could be more than one solution, but we were only interested in finding one. In this example we do not know whether there is a matching entry in the table; that is what we want to find out. The function is not continuous (it is a set of points, or *discrete* values), but it is monotonic, so we can decide on the basis of an inspection of the middle entry whether the "zero," if there is one, is to the left or the right of the middle point. In Figure 1-6, the entry at the middle point is larger than the entry being sought, so it is clear that if the latter is present, it must be to the left, or in the lower part of the list. Thus, in one step we have halved the size of the list to be examined further.

The similarity between this example and the previous one is sufficient that they can be solved by very similar programs. The only major difference is the stopping criterion, which in the previous example was an accuracy criterion based on the difference between LOW and HIGH. In this example, LOW and HIGH must be integers, and the stopping criterion must be related to the size of the remaining part of the table: when there is nothing to be halved further, we can stop, because the entry is obviously absent. Therefore, we can change the stopping criterion so that we finish when LOW > HIGH. We can stop sooner if we find a matching entry in the table. This requires an additional test within the loop, as shown in Program 1-3. In this program the use of integer arithmetic for

■ **Program 1.3   Binary search method**

```
BINARYSEARCH: program
    Program to find whether an entry is in an ordered array, and if it is
    present, the index of its entry. TABLE(I), I = 1, . . . N is
    assumed to be the array of N objects. The object being sought is
    assumed to be in variable SOUGHT. The types of the values in
    TABLE and SOUGHT should be the same—for example, character
    strings or integers.
    integer LOW,HIGH,MID
    LOW ← 1
    HIGH ← N
    do while HIGH ≥ LOW
        MID ← (LOW + HIGH)/2
        if TABLE(MID) = SOUGHT
            then exit loop
            else if TABLE(MID) below SOUGHT
                then LOW ← MID+1
                else HIGH ← MID−1
                endif
            endif
        enddo
    if SOUGHT = TABLE(MID)
        then entry SOUGHT has been found
        else entry SOUGHT not present
    endprogram
```

those variables used as indices in the array is critical. Note that at each stage we reduce the size of the remaining table to be inspected by more than a factor of 2, because after dividing it in two (to within one entry) we exclude the middle entry from the reduced table by using either MID + 1 or MID − 1, as appropriate. This can be done because we have already verified that the entry is not at the middle point. That the table decreases in size by at least one entry on every loop guarantees that eventually we will reduce it to a size of zero.

This type of approach is sometimes called a divide and conquer method, because it divides the problem into smaller ones. If we start with a table of three entries, so that LOW and HIGH are initially 1 and 3, MID will be set to 2. If that is not the entry sought, then LOW and HIGH will become either 1 and 1, or 3 and 3, depending on the comparison of SOUGHT and TABLE(2). Thus, the remaining table size is 1. Similarly, if the initial table size is 7, it is reduced to 3 in one step, and 1 in two steps. The method is much faster than the sequential search discussed in Example 1.2, as can be seen by considering a fairly large table. Suppose, for example, we had a table of 1023 elements. In successive steps it would be reduced as follows:

Step Number	Remaining Table Size
0	1023
1	511
2	255
3	127
4	63
5	31
6	15
7	7
8	3
9	1
10	0

Hence, a maximum of nine passes through the loop would suffice to determine whether the entry was present. A sequential search could take 1023 passes for the same task; although each pass is faster because there is less work (one comparison instead of two, and simpler arithmetic), the need for more than a hundred-fold more passes makes the sequential method much slower.

Unfortunately, the binary search method requires a sorted list. Because it is so much faster than the sequential search, we might ask whether it is better to sort a table before searching it. In Part I of this book we will see that sorting methods are slower than related searching methods. However, if we want to search in a table many times, it may well be worth paying the price of sorting it first to speed up the many subsequent searches. Here we see that there is more than one method for solving a problem and that the choice of method may depend on the context in which it will be used.

1.2 A SUMMARY OF PROBLEM-SOLVING TECHNIQUES

We have introduced by example a number of methods that are typical of general problem-solving techniques. They are

Direct computation

Simulation

Enumeration (try all cases)

Iteration (trial and error)

Repeated reduction to smaller problem

Divide and conquer

Direct computation, as used in Example 1.1, is simply the use of the computer to evaluate a formula that we have found (or generated) to solve the problem. It will give the fastest method of solution but is applicable to a limited class of numerical problems. Simulation here refers to the direct implementation on the computer of the process as it actually happens. In Example 1.1 we initially simulated the action of a bank in paying interest before we found a way of directly computing it. Simulation is restricted to those problems that we essentially already know how to solve; it just suggests a way of implementing a computer program to compute the solution. Enumeration can be used whenever a solution can be found by checking a finite number of cases—that is, if it is always possible to tell whether a particular case is the solution and we have a way of counting through all cases. The sequential search is an example of this method. However, enumeration is usually the slowest method and should be used only if no other can be found. Iteration is an important method for numerical problems, although it sometimes finds use in other areas. It usually depends on the ability to compute the "error" in the current approximation—that is, the amount by which the current approximation differs from the solution—and to use this amount to adjust the current approximation in a way that will bring it closer to the solution. The analysis of these methods usually depends on some substantial mathematics, which we will not pursue.

Most problems cannot be immediately handled by any of the first four methods, so it is necessary to subdivide the problem into a set of simpler problems, or reduce the problem to the solution of a simpler problem.

The art of problem solving is the skill in finding ways to subdivide problems, which is learned by exposure to many methods and by practice.

Problem reduction takes one of two forms. First, we may reduce the problem to a simpler one of the same form. In this case we can apply the reduction repeatedly until the problem is simple enough to solve directly. That is essentially what we did in Examples 1.3, 1.5, and 1.6 for the greatest common divisor, the method of bisection, and the binary search. We should always be on the lookout for ways to "make a problem smaller," because this can provide a very fast method.

In the second form of reduction, we reduce a problem to a sequence of simpler problems, each of which must be solved to compute the overall solution. For example, if the problem is to compute a person's income tax, given the tax rules, the number of hours the person has worked, and the rate of pay, we might decide to compute the person's wages first, and then to compute the tax from the wages. In a sense we have reduced the original problem to a pair of simpler problems. Our first few examples are simple in that they can be solved essentially by a single technique applied one or more times. Most large problems must be reduced to a set of simpler, different problems, because they cannot be solved by a single technique. Each subproblem is solved in turn, yielding intermediate results that lead toward the overall solution. For example, for the trivial tax problem in this paragraph, the intermediate result was the person's wages. When looking for a method for solving a problem, we try to determine what would be useful intermediate results. These immediately suggest a breakdown into subproblems. If we decide that the person's wages are a useful intermediate result in the tax problem, then we have reduced the original problem to two simpler ones: compute the person's wages, given the hours worked and the rate of pay, and then compute the tax, given the tax rules and the wages.

The selection of an intermediate result as a *subgoal* of the solution process is an important step. Choosing the right subgoal can make the solution easy to find, whereas choosing the wrong one can result in hours of work wasted in trying to solve irrelevant or impossible subproblems. Usually it is better to start with the answer and ask the question, What do I need to know to compute this answer? This question may suggest some subgoals. We could also start with the data given for the problem and ask what we could easily compute from it; but this is more likely to send us off in the wrong direction, because there may be many more things computable from the given data than are asked for in the problem statement.

It is important to determine whether enough information has been provided to solve a given problem. As we have seen, problem statements frequently contain assumptions that are not explicitly stated. Even if all assumptions are explicitly stated, it is still possible that we have been given an inadequate amount of data to solve the problem, and it may be very difficult to determine that fact (because such a determination would essentially amount to a mathematical proof that the problem could not be solved). In some cases the lack of data may be obvious. For example, if you are asked to compute a person's tax but are not told how much that person has earned, the problem clearly cannot be solved. In other cases, one may mistakenly decide that there is insufficient data and ask for more. If the additional data happens to be available anyway, no harm is done and it can be used. In many real-world situations there may be more data available than needed to solve the problem. If it is possible to solve the problem with the data initially provided, a more efficient solution may nevertheless be possible with some additional data. Even if no further data is available, nothing is lost, since somebody may suggest a way of computing it from available data.

In the real world, it is more likely that too much data is available, and the problem solver may be confused by an abundance of information. This is an important reason for working backward from the final goal to the data originally given, since this procedure will determine what data should be used. (Problems given to students frequently contain just enough data for the solution and no more, so many students get into the habit of making sure that they have "used all the data." This is a dangerous practice when the instructor tosses in a few irrelevant facts, and is an unreasonable practice in real-world problems.)

No amount of discussion of problem-solving techniques, however, will teach a person to solve problems, so it is time to start examining some real methods and practicing solving simple problems. As you do this in subsequent chapters, try to relate the methods to those you have already seen, and think of similar problems you could solve with these methods.

Referenced Material and Other Reading

Duncker, K. 1945. On problem solving. *Psychological Monographs* **58** (5, Whole number 270).

Polya, G. 1954a. *Mathematics and plausible reasoning*, vol. 1, *Induction and analogy in mathematics*. Princeton, N.J.: Princeton University Press.

——— 1954b. *Mathematics and plausible reasoning*, vol. 2, *Patterns of plausible inference*. Princeton, N.J.: Princeton University Press.

——— 1957. *How to solve it*, 2nd ed. Garden City, N.Y.: Doubleday & Company.

——— 1962. *Mathematical discovery, on understanding learning and teaching problem solving*, vol. 1. New York: John Wiley.

——— 1965. *Mathematical discovery, on understanding learning and teaching problem solving*, vol. 2. New York: John Wiley.

Wickelgren, W. A. 1974. *How to solve problems*. San Francisco: W. H. Freeman.

PROBLEMS

1 What is the maximum number of items that can be searched with a binary search if no more than

    a. 3

    b. 4

    c. 6

    d. n

comparisons can be used in the worst case? (Assume that one comparison will determine whether one value is smaller than, equal to, or larger than another.)

2 If a single pass through a sequential search loop takes 2 microseconds and a single pass through a binary search loop takes 21 microseconds, construct a graph showing the worst-case search time for each method versus the number of items in an array. For what number of items N will the binary search method be faster?

I

SEARCHING AND SORTING

■   ■   ■   ■

One of the principal functions of a computer is to organize and access information. Searching and sorting are major tools in this process. In the introductory chapter we examined two simple examples of searching. We saw that the simplest method, the sequential search, demanded no particular organization of the data, but that it was much slower than the binary search, which required that the data be sorted. Because the retrieval of data can be much faster if it is sorted, sorting is a very important function. In Part I, we examine several sorting methods and also several ways of storing the structure of data that are useful in searching and sorting.

When we organize a computer program or design a method for the solution of a problem, we must keep in mind the way in which it is going to be used: which parts of the program will be used extensively, and which parts hardly at all. The former parts should execute as rapidly as possible, and we should design the storage of data so that the information needed is readily available. The latter parts are less important: for them it is necessary only to organize the data so that a solution is possible in a reasonable length of time.

Although searching, sorting, and data-structuring techniques are more important to nonnumerical processing, they are also very important adjuncts to numerical processing, because in most large-scale scientific and engineering calculations a considerable amount of time is spent manipulating a computer representation of the problem to be solved.

C H A P T E R

2

Sorting
in Arrays

■   ■   ■   ■   ■   ■   ■

Arrays are convenient for storing many forms of data, because they allow the access of any entry via its index. In this chapter we shall look at several methods for sorting data held in one-dimensional arrays. Although the data can consist of anything that is *totally ordered*—that is, any type of data for which relations such as "greater than" and "less than" make sense—to be specific, we will assume that we are sorting numerical data.

The first group of sorting methods we will look at are all types of *sequential* methods. They keep scanning through the data from one end to the other, moving entries that are out of order into position. They are conceptually simple and easy to code, and for small amounts of data they are very effective. However, as with sequential searching methods, they become slow for large amounts of data. We will therefore also examine a type of binary sort that provides the same degree of speedup over the sequential sort as the binary search provides over the sequential search.

The first method we will examine is called the *selection sort*. Suppose we want to sort an *N*-entry array into ascending order. We first find the smallest entry and move it into the first position, by switching it with the

FIGURE 2-1 Stages of selection sort

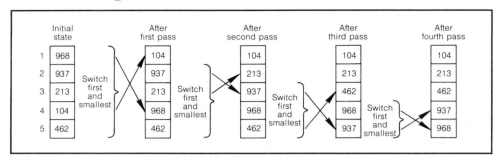

■ **Program 2.1** **Selection sort**

```
SELECT_SORT: program
        Program to sort an integer array into ascending order using a
        selection sort. The contents of the array ID and its dimension N are
        assumed given.
        integer K,N,ID(N)
            do for K ← 1 to N − 1
                First K − 1 elements are now in order. Find smallest
                remaining element and move it to position K.
                set I to index of smallest element between
                    ID(K) and ID(N)
                switch ID(I) and ID(K)
            enddo
endprogram SELECT_SORT
```

element originally in that position. Then we know that the first element is correct, and we can proceed in the same way to sort the remaining $N - 1$ elements in positions 2 through N of the array. This process is shown in Figure 2-1 for $N = 5$. Each successive pass moves one more element into position. After $N - 1$ passes, the array will be in order. The overall form of the algorithm is shown in Program 2-1. Each pass through the outer loop moves the smallest element of the array ID(I), for I from K to N, into position ID(K). All that remains is to "refine" the two steps of finding the smallest value in the subarray and switching the elements. Those sections of code are shown in the refined version, Program 2-1a.

The sorting algorithm of Program 2-1a requires a long time to execute. On the first pass through the outer loop, the inner loop is executed for I from 2 to N; on the second pass, from 3 to N; and so on. The total number

■ Program 2.1a   Further refinement of Program 2-1

```
SELECT_SORT: program
     Program to sort an integer array into ascending order using a
     selection sort. The contents of the array ID and its dimension N are
     assumed given.
     integer I,J,K,N,ID(N),SMALL
        do for K ← 1 to N − 1
              First K − 1 elements are now in order. Find smallest
              remaining element and move it to position K.
              I ← K
              SMALL ← ID(K)
              do for J ← K + 1 to N
                    SMALL contains smallest element between ID(K)
                    and ID(J − 1). I is its index.
                    if ID(J) < SMALL
                       then I ← J
                            SMALL ← ID(J)
                       endif
                 enddo
              ID(I) ← ID(K)
              ID(K) ← SMALL
           enddo
     endprogram SELECT_SORT
```

of passes needed through the inner loop is thus $(N − 1) + (N − 2) + (N − 3) + \cdots + 3 + 2 + 1$, which comes to $N \times (N − 1)/2$.* If N is 100, this means the inner loop must be executed 4950 times, regardless of the original order of the data; even if it is already in order and needs no sorting, 4950 passes through the inner loop are still required.

The observation that the sorting method just described can take a long time even if the elements are already in order prompts us to look for

---

*This can be seen by writing the series once in the order given and once in reverse:

$$(N − 1) + (N − 2) + (N − 3) + \cdots + 3 + 2 + 1$$
$$1 + 2 + 3 + \cdots + (N − 3) + (N − 2) + (N − 1)$$

Adding term by term, we find that twice the sum of the series is

$$N + N + N + \cdots + N + N + N$$

Since there are $N − 1$ terms, twice the sum of the series is $N \times (N − 1)$, so the sum of the series is $N \times (N − 1)/2$.

FIGURE 2-2 First pass of a bubble sort

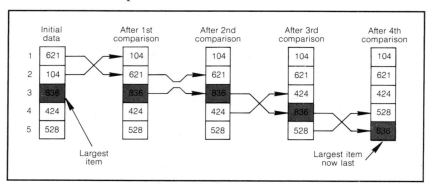

methods that are faster when the data is already sorted or nearly so. The next method we examine is called the *bubble sort*. On each pass through the list, each pair of adjacent items is compared: if they are in the proper order they are left alone and the next pair is examined; if they are out of order they are switched before going on to the next pair. The process is illustrated in Figure 2-2, which shows the following steps:

1. Compare the first pair, 621 and 104. They are out of order, so switch them.
2. Compare the second pair, 621 and 836. They are already in order, so leave them alone.
3. Compare the third pair, 836 and 424. They are out of order, so switch them.
4. Compare the fourth pair, 836 and 528. They are out of order, so switch them.

As a result of these operations, at the end of the first pass the largest element in the list, 836, has "bubbled" to the last position. The next pass will work with the first $N - 1$ elements, and will move the next largest to the next-to-last position, and so on. Notice that if an N-element list is already sorted to begin with, we will find this out on the first pass, after only $N - 1$ comparisons—the minimum possible to determine that N elements are already sorted.

The bubble-sort algorithm is shown in Program 2-2. I is the loop counter, and is decremented from N to 2 on successive passes through the outer loop. On each pass, the counter for the inner loop, J, need run only from 1 to $I - 1$, since the last $N - I$ positions already contain the $N - I$ largest elements. At most, $N - 1$ passes through the outer loop are needed to sort the list into ascending order, but it may take fewer: if no switches are made on any given pass, then we are finished. Accordingly, a variable K is used to remember whether any switches have yet been made

■ **Program 2.2   Bubble sort**

```
BUBBLE_SORT: program
```
Program to sort an integer array into ascending order using a bubble sort. The contents of the array ID and its dimension N are assumed given.
```
integer I,J,K,N,ID(N),TEMP
    I ← N
    K ← 1
```
The flag K is nonzero on the first pass of the outer loop and whenever switches were made on the previous pass.
```
    do while I ≥ 2 and K ≠ 0
```
The largest N − 1 elements of ID are now in order in positions ID (I + 1) to ID(N). Float the largest of the first I elements to position ID(I).
```
        K ← 0
        do for J ← 1 to I − 1
```
The largest of the first J elements is now in position ID(J).
```
            if ID(J) > ID(J + 1)
                then
```
Switch entries ID(J) and ID(J + 1).
```
                    TEMP ← ID(J)
                    ID(J) ← ID(J + 1)
                    ID(J + 1) ← TEMP
                    K ← 1
            endif
        enddo
        I ← I − 1
    enddo
endprogram BUBBLE_SORT
```

on the current pass: it is set to zero at the beginning of the pass and changed to nonzero whenever a switch is made. If K is still zero at the beginning of the next pass, the outer loop terminates; otherwise it terminates when I becomes less than 2.

In the best case, when the data is already in order, the bubble sort takes only one scan through the list, and no sorting method can do better. However, in the worst case, the bubble sort takes a maximum of $N \times (N − 1)/2$ comparisons, as does any sequential method. (The worst case occurs when the data is in reverse order: a bubble sort of 5, 4, 3, 2, 1 into ascending order requires 10 switches. After the first pass through the outer loop, four switches have been made and the list is 4, 3, 2, 1, 5.) Furthermore, in the worst case, each of these comparisons will cause a

FIGURE 2-3 Insertion sort

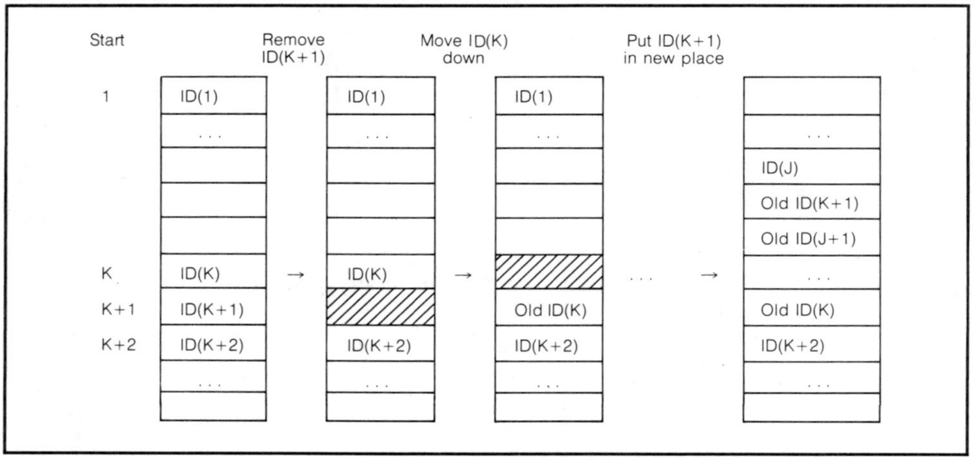

switch of two data items (which requires three assignment statements), compared with the maximum of $N - 1$ switches needed in the selection sort described earlier. Thus, although the bubble sort is faster than the earlier method in the best case, it is slower in the worst case.

The third sequential sorting method we will consider is the *insertion sort*, illustrated in Figure 2-3. In this method, the list is scanned until an out-of-order element is found. The scan is then temporarily halted while a backward scan is made to find the point at which to insert the out-of-order element. Elements bypassed during this backward scan are moved up one position to make room for the element being inserted. Thus, in Figure 2-3, if the first K elements are in order but the $K + 1$st is not—that is, if ID(1) ≤ ID(2) ≤ ID(3) ≤ $\cdots$ ≤ ID(K) but ID(K) > ID(K + 1)— then ID(K + 1) is out of order and must be moved to an earlier position. It is removed from the array (that is, a copy of its value is saved somewhere, say at TEMP) and the elements ID(K), ID(K − 1), . . . are examined until an ID(J) is found such that ID(J) ≤ old ID(K + 1). In the process, the old elements ID(J + 1) through ID(K) will have been moved to positions ID(J + 2) through ID(K + 1), clearing the J + 1st position for the value saved at TEMP.

Program 2-3 is based on this method. The inner loop is in the **then** clause of an **if** statement, and is executed only when an out-of-order element is found. Like the bubble sort, the insertion sort is a sequential sort technique. Like the bubble sort, it requires only $N - 1$ comparisons in the best case (when the data is already sorted initially); again like the bubble sort, it requires $N \times (N - 1)/2$ comparisons and moves in the worst case—but unlike the bubble sort, it completes each move in only one assignment statement instead of three.

■ **Program 2.3   Insertion sort**

```
INSERT_SORT: program
     Program to sort an integer array into ascending order using an
     insertion sort. The contents of the array ID and its dimension N
     are assumed given.
     integer J,K,N,ID(N),TEMP
         do for K ← I to N − 1
             ID(1) to ID(K) are now in ascending order. Extend to
             ID(K + 1).
             if ID(K) > ID(K + 1)
                 then
                     Move ID(K + 1) back to its place in array.
                     First save its value in TEMP, then move earlier
                     elements up one place until the right position is
                     found.
                     TEMP ← ID(K + 1)
                     J ← K
                     do while J ≥ 1 and ID(J) > TEMP
                         ID(J + 1) ← ID(J)
                         J ← J − 1
                         enddo
                     ID(J + 1) ← TEMP
                 endif
             enddo
     endprogram INSERT_SORT
```

2.1 BINARY SORTING

Any method of sorting based on a sequential search through an N-element list for the largest remaining element will take time proportional to N^2, as do the three methods discussed so far. This means that the execution time increases rapidly as N gets large. We saw earlier that the sequential search becomes progressively worse compared to the binary search as N gets large. There are, in fact, sorting methods that employ techniques similar to those used in a binary search and are faster than sequential methods for large amounts of data.

A binary technique can often be developed using a divide and conquer approach to the problem. In the binary search we divided the table (array) of entries into two subtables and discarded one of them. In the sorting process we cannot discard any of the entries, because all must be sorted. However, if we divide the table of entries into two subtables and then sort each subtable separately, we may have simplified the problem, since each of the subtables is smaller. Now consider the state of the table

FIGURE 2-4 Sorted subtables

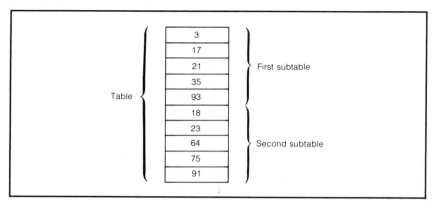

after each of the subtables has been sorted separately. It could appear as in Figure 2-4, in which the full table is not sorted, even though the two subtables are sorted. Had all the entries in the first subtable been less than or equal to all of the entries in the second subtable, the full table would have been sorted after each subtable had been sorted. Thus, if we want the full table to be sorted, we have two choices: either we initially arrange for the first subtable to have all its entries less than or equal to those in the second subtable or we combine the two subtables after they have been sorted to get a sorted result. The second approach leads to a *merge sort*, to be discussed in Section 3.3. The first approach leads to the method known as *Quicksort*. In this method, we first scan through the table, moving entries to divide it into two subtables such that all entries in the first subtable are less than or equal to all in the second subtable. We say that we have *partitioned* the table. Each subtable is then sorted by exactly the same technique unless it has length 1, in which case it is already sorted.

How can we partition the table into two parts? Ideally, we would like the parts to have about the same size. If we knew the *median* entry in the table (that is, the entry for which the number of entries less than it is within one of the number greater than it), we could put those entries less than or equal to the median in the first part of the table and those entries greater than the median in the second part of the table. Unfortunately, computing the median of a table is time consuming, so instead of using the median we pick an entry "at random"—for example, the entry physically in the middle of the table—and then partition the table so that the first values are less than or equal to the chosen entry, and the last values are greater than or equal to it. The partitioning can be performed by scanning the table from each end in turn to detect entries that are in the wrong half, and switching out-of-order entries. This is illustrated in Figure 2-5. Figure 2-5a shows a seven-entry, unsorted table. Its middle entry, 51, is selected as a basis for the partition. A scan begins from the first entry and continues down until the first entry not less than 51 is encountered. In this example it is the second entry, 95, as indicated in Figure 2-5b by the pointer F. Now a scan starts from the bottom of the table and moves up, looking for the entry nearest the end that is not larger than 51. This is found at the entry whose value is 47, as shown in Figure 2-5c by the pointer B. The entries with values 95 and 47 are switched and both pointers are moved to the next entries in their respective scans, as shown in Figure 2-5d, after which the process continues. In this example, the forward scan reaches the entry with value 51, as shown in Figure 2-5e, and then the backward scan resumes, only to stop immediately because it is already at the entry 12, which is smaller than 51. The entries 51 and 12 are switched and the pointers moved on to the positions shown in Figure 2-5f. Now the forward-scan pointer has passed the backward-scan pointer, so the process must stop. The table has been divided into two subtables: the first subtable ends at the final position of the backward-scan pointer; the second subtable begins at the final position of the forward-scan pointer.

After one partition we have divided the table of Figure 2-5a into the two subtables shown in Figure 2-6a, each of which is now treated similarly. We select 33 as the middle entry of the first subtable in Figure 2-6a. The forward scan reaches 47 and the backward scan stops at 12. These entries are switched and the scan pointers moved so that both now point at 33. Both scans now stop on the 33 entry. The entries are switched (an unnecessary action, but it does no harm), and the scan pointers are moved past each other so that F points to 47 and B points to 12. Hence, the first subtable contains 27 and 12, and the second contains 47. The entry 33 lies between them and is in its correct final position. Figures 2-6b

FIGURE 2-5 Stages of a partition step

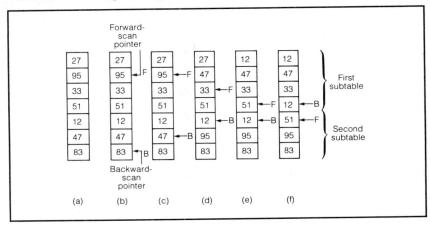

FIGURE 2-6 Next 2 levels of partitions

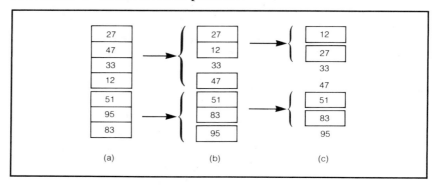

(a)   (b)   (c)

and 2-6c illustrate the result of partitioning at each of the next levels. The subtables are indicated in boxes. When a subtable has length 1, it is sorted and so no longer needs to be partitioned.

How fast is this method? Let us suppose for a moment that we could break a table into two equally sized subtables with the desired property. If we started with a table containing two entries, one partitioning would yield two subtables, each of length 1, which are necessarily sorted. The number of steps is proportional to N, the length of the table. Similarly, if we started with four entries, the first partition would give us two subtables of length 2. After each of these has been partitioned, the table will be sorted. Note that any partitioning to one further level of subdivision examines each entry once, so it will take N steps. Consequently, the total number of operations is proportional to N times the number of levels of partitioning necessary. If the tables are subdivided into two essentially equal subtables at each step, the number of levels of partitioning will be the number of times we have to divide N by 2 to get no more than 1. This is the smallest integer no less than $\log_2 N$. Hence, Quicksort takes approximately $N \log_2 N$ operations in the case of equal subdivision. This is the best (fastest) case for the method. In the slowest case, each table is divided into a table of length one and a table of length one less than was started with. In this case, Quicksort has a running time proportional to N^2. However, it has been shown that, on the average, Quicksort has a running time proportional to $N \log_2 N$ and is one of the fastest methods for large tables.

PROBLEMS

1 What arrangements of the integers 1, 2, 3, 4, and 5 in a five-entry array will lead to a worst-case sort time for the insertion sort in Program 2-3?

2 What is the answer to Problem 1 for the bubble sort in Program 2-2?

3 Write a program to do the table subdivision step of the Quicksort method. Your program should start with an array $W(I)$, $I = 1, \ldots, N$ of integers and a value V. At the end of execution you should have moved the entries of W and computed an index K such that for all $1 \leq I \leq K$, $W(I) \leq V$ and for all $K + 1 \leq I \leq N$, $W(I) \geq V$.

4 Construct examples of seven-entry tables that lead to the best-case and worst-case sort times for Quicksort, respectively.

3

Searching
and Sorting
with Pointers

In the previous chapter we discussed sorting data held in arrays. Arrays provide the ability to access any item immediately by index and, when they can be used directly, usually lead to the fastest algorithms. However, it is not always convenient to store and modify data in arrays. If more flexibility for data movement is required, we often use *pointers*. A pointer is a data type that is used to indicate the position of, or point to, another data value. Many languages have a special data type called pointer, but it is possible to program with pointer-like variables in languages that do not have a special pointer type. Usually the simplest way to do this is to use an integer type for a pointer value and let it be the index in an array of values to be pointed at. Because the way pointer data types are handled is very language dependent, we will discuss pointers here as if they were integers.

Pointers can be used to construct lists. The word "list" is used both in a general way with its common meaning and in a precise way meaning a collection of values that can be accessed only sequentially—that is, one after another. In this chapter we will discuss the use of pointers and lists in the searching and sorting process and describe some very important types of lists.

3.1 POINTERS

The sorting techniques discussed in Chapter 2 required moving data around to put it in the right order. If each data item is large (occupies a large number of memory cells), this movement can absorb large amounts of computer time. Suppose, for example, that we have two arrays: ID(I) contains the ID number of the *I*th student, and SCORE(I,J) contains the *I*th student's score on the *J*th exam. If we use any of the sorting methods presented in Chapter 2 to sort the data by student ID number, we will have to swap two whole rows in the array SCORE every time we swap a pair of elements in ID. If we don't, we will lose track of the correspondence between elements of ID and rows of SCORE.

We can overcome this difficulty by using an auxiliary array of *pointers* to ID and SCORE. Thus we will use an integer array INDEX whose elements are indices into the arrays ID and SCORE. When we sort the student records into ascending order by ID number, we can simply move the indices in INDEX instead of moving the data itself in ID and SCORE. The method is depicted in Figure 3-1. The first three columns show the state of the arrays before the data is sorted; the last three show the arrays after the sort is completed. Notice that only the elements of the array INDEX have been moved; ID and SCORE remain unchanged. To print the student data in order by ID number, we simply step through the array INDEX, using each successive element as an index to help us find the entries to be printed next in ID and SCORE.

FIGURE 3-1 Sorting using pointers in INDEX

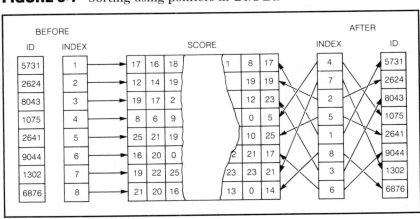

3.2 LISTS

Pointers are a means for accessing data in memory without searching for it, and are one of the most important ideas in programming. They can be used in a variety of ways, in both business and scientific applications, to make programs more efficient. In those applications to which they are suited, they can also make a program conceptually cleaner and easier to read.

Suppose we are writing an airline reservation system and want to keep a list of the names of the passengers on each flight. There is a separate such list for each flight, and each of these lists is constantly changing as reservations are made and canceled. (We will not concern ourselves in this discussion with the way in which character strings are handled—we will simply assume that we can use an array NAME to store the passenger names for a flight. We will also assume we know the maximum size such a list can have—presumably the number of seats on the plane—so that we can allocate the right size array.)

Initially our array NAME is empty. As reservations are made on the flight, each new name can be added in the next available empty location in the array. To keep track of this location we will use a variable, say AVAIL, which is initially set to 1 (pointing to the first element of the array). To add a new name to the list, we store it at NAME(AVAIL) and increase AVAIL by 1. Deleting an entry causes problems, however, because it leaves a "hole" in the array. We would like to use this space for another passenger, so we must either keep track of the holes or move the existing data around, as in Figure 3-2, to fill the holes as they are created. The latter alternative can be quite time-consuming, since half the entries (on the average) must be moved every time an entry is deleted. If the data is ordered, entries must be moved in this way to do insertions as well as deletions.

FIGURE 3-2 Deleting an entry in an array

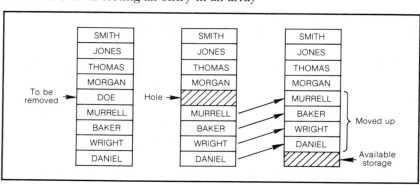

FIGURE 3-3 Information stored with pointers

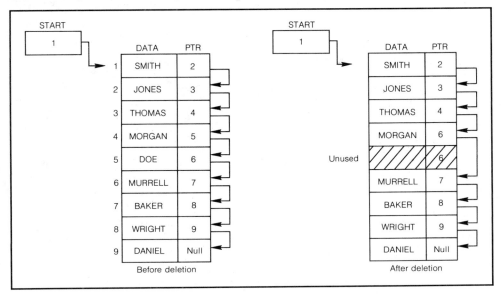

Once again, pointers provide the solution. This time we use them to construct a data structure called a *chained* or *linked list*, in which each entry carries a pointer to the next (see Figure 3-3). To scan the list in order, we begin with variable START, which points to the first item in the list; thereafter, each item we examine tells us where to find the next item. The end of the list is marked by a special "null" pointer, which can be represented by any recognizable value, such as zero. Using this data structure we can delete an item without leaving a "hole" in the list, simply by copying the pointer from that item into the item preceding it in the list, so that it "points around" the deleted item. In Figure 3-3, for example, we delete the name DOE from the list by copying its pointer (6) into the entry containing the name MORGAN, so that MORGAN points "around" DOE to MURRELL. To remove the last entry, DANIEL, we would copy its null pointer into the entry containing WRIGHT; to remove the first entry, SMITH, we would copy its pointer (2) into the variable START.

Notice, however, that in order to find the item preceding a given item, say DOE, in the list, we have to begin with the variable START and scan the list in order until we find an item pointing to DOE. Notice also that we cannot easily access a random element in the middle of the list, since the *I*th element need not be stored in the *I*th location in the array. To find the *I*th element, we must again run through the list from the beginning, counting elements as we go until we reach the one we want. Thus the use of a chained list makes some operations (deleting an element, scanning the list in sequence) easier or more efficient and others (accessing the *I*th element) harder or less efficient. It also uses more memory space, since room must be allocated for the pointers as well as the data items themselves. The decision whether to use such a list depends on how often we expect to be performing the various operations.

Note that a chained list can be searched only sequentially, even if the entries in the list are sorted. This restriction arises because it is not possible to locate entries other than the first without counting from the start of the list and visiting each entry in turn. If we do that, we have lost the advantage of any method, such as binary search, that relies on the ability to access a particular entry such as the middle one.

Figures 3-4 and 3-5 depict the operations of deleting an element from the middle and the beginning of a list, respectively. From now on we will draw chained lists as shown in these figures. We do not know or care where the list items actually are in memory in relation to each other, because the pointers always tell us where the next item is.

When we add an item to a list, we can insert it anywhere we want in the chain of pointers connecting the list elements. If there is no reason to put it in any particular place, the front of the list is the easiest place to reach. Adding a new entry CAR to the front of a list containing MAP, TEMP, and B1 is shown in Figure 3-6. No data has to be moved: the pointer that was in START is simply put into the new entry, and START is set to point to this new entry.

FIGURE 3-4 Removing an item from a list

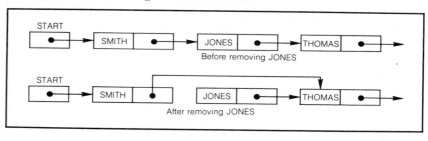

FIGURE 3-5 Removing the first item from a list

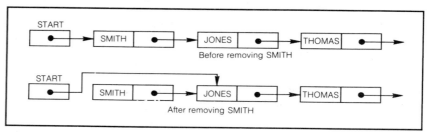

FIGURE 3-6 Inserting a new entry to the beginning of a list

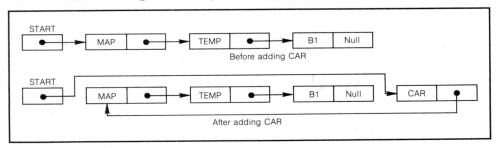

FIGURE 3-7 Inserting a new entry in alphabetical order

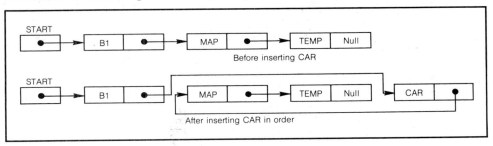

If a list is to be kept in sorted order, a sequential search is necessary to find the appropriate position for the new entry. Once the position is found, however, the new entry can be inserted without moving existing data: we need only set the pointer of the preceding entry to point to the new one, and set the pointer of the new one to point to the next one, as shown in Figure 3-7.

Each entry in Figures 3-4 through 3-7 is shown as a doublet. It could be a pair of adjacent memory cells or a pair of corresponding positions in two arrays: an array of character strings for the names and an array of integers for the pointers. We will call these arrays DATA and PTR, respectively. They are shown side by side in Figure 3-8.

To add an entry to a chained list, we must find storage space for the new entry. The simplest method is sequential storage assignment: we initially assign an area of memory for the list and note that the first word in this area is currently available. As each entry is placed into the list, the first available locations in the assigned area are taken for the entry, as shown in Figure 3-8. AVAIL contains the address of the first available location in the storage area. When CAR is logically inserted at the front of the list containing MAP and B1, AVAIL and START are both updated appropriately.

FIGURE 3-8 Available memory locations

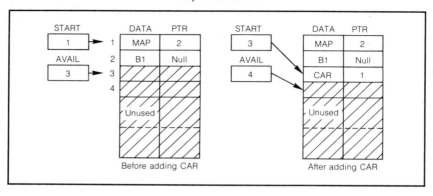

Before adding CAR   After adding CAR

FIGURE 3-9 Lost storage

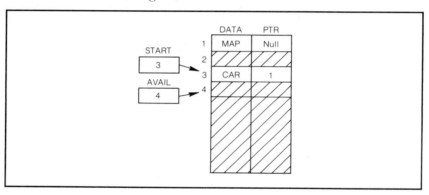

FIGURE 3-10 Use of free-storage pointer

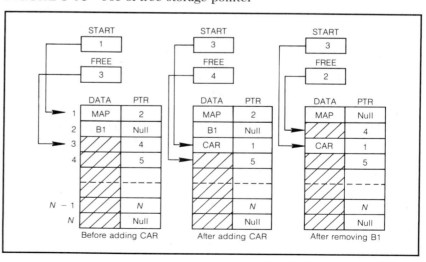

Before adding CAR   After adding CAR   After removing B1

When an entry is removed from the list, the storage it occupied is lost in this method unless it happens to be physically the last. Thus, if `B1` is removed from the list in Figure 3-8, we get the list shown in Figure 3-9. `DATA(2)` and `PTR(2)` are unused, but there is no simple way of reusing them for the next entry. We can solve this problem by keeping the unused space on a *free-storage list*, or *free list*. A variable, say `FREE`, can be used to hold a pointer to an unused element. That element can contain a pointer to another unused element, and so on. Initially, all available storage space must be put on the free list. This can be done by setting `FREE` to 1, `PTR(I)` to $I + 1$ for $1 \le I \le N - 1$, and `PTR(N)` to `NULL`. When an element is added to the list, space can be taken from the beginning of the free storage list; when an element is removed, the space released can be added to the free list. The steps needed to add `CAR` and then remove `B1` are shown in Figure 3-10.

Programs 3-1 through 3-4 are subprograms to initialize the free list, insert a name in alphabetical order, delete a name, and output the list in order. One change has been made to the process described above: the

■ **Program 3.1   Initialize list pointers**

```
INIT_LIST: subprogram (PTR,N,AVAIL)
    integer I,N,PTR(N),AVAIL
    Initialize list head and start of free list.
        AVAIL ← 2
        PTR(1) ← 0
    Set pointers for free list.
        do for I ← 2 to N - 1
            PTR (I) ← I + 1
        enddo
    Set null pointer at end of free list.
        PTR(N) ← 0
        return
    endsubprogram INIT_LIST
```

■ **Program 3.2   Insert element in ordered list**

```
INSERT: subprogram (DATA,PTR,N,AVAIL,NAME)
    Program to insert the name NAME in the alphabetically ordered list
    contained in arrays DATA and PTR. Head of data list assumed to
    be in PTR(1), head of free list in AVAIL.
    integer I,J,N,PTR(N),AVAIL
        if AVAIL = 0
            then output 'NO FREE STORAGE LEFT'
            else
```

```
                I ← 1
                Search list for insertion point for NAME.
                do while PTR(I) ≠ 0 and DATA(PTR(I)) <
                    NAME
                    I ← PTR(I)
                    enddo
                I now contains entry of last element in list less than
                NAME. Allocate space from free list for new entry
                and insert it following entry I by setting pointers.
                J ← AVAIL
                AVAIL ← PTR(J)
                PTR(J) ← PTR(I)
                DATA(J) ← NAME
                PTR(I) ← J
            endif
        return
    endsubprogram INSERT
```

■ **Program 3.3   Delete element from chained list**

```
DELETE: subprogram (DATA,PTR,N,AVAIL,NAME)
    Program to delete the name NAME from the chained list contained
    in arrays DATA and PTR. If NAME is present, it is removed from
    data list and the space it occupies returned to free list; if not
    present, an error message is printed. Head of data list assumed to
    be in PTR(1), head of free list in AVAIL.
    integer I,J,N,PTR(N),AVAIL
        I ← 1
        Find NAME in data list.
        do while PTR(I) ≠ 0 and DATA (PTR(I)) ≠ NAME
            I ← PTR(I)
            enddo
        if PTR(I) = 0
            then output 'NAME',NAME,'NOT PRESENT IN
                LIST'
            else
                Entry following I now contains NAME. Fix pointers
                to delete it from data list and put it on free list.
                J ← PTR(I)
                PTR(I) ← PTR(J)
                PTR(J) ← AVAIL
                AVAIL ← J
            endif
        return
    endsubprogram DELETE
```

■ **Program 3.4   Print chained list in order**

```
PRINT_LIST: subprogram (DATA,PTR,N)
    Program to print the chained list contained in arrays DATA and
    PTR. List head assumed to be in PTR(I).
    integer I,N,PTR(N)
        I ← PTR(1)
        do while I ≠ 0
            output DATA(I)
            I ← PTR(I)
            enddo
        return
    endsubprogram PRINT_LIST
```

pointer to the start of the data list is kept in PTR(1), which means that DATA(1) is not used. This avoids a number of complications in the special case of an empty list. (The reader can see this by rewriting Programs 3-2 and 3-3, using the variable START instead of PTR(1).) The pointer we are keeping in PTR(1) is sometimes called the *list head*.

Notice that the **do while** statements in Programs 3-2 and 3-3 may cause problems on some systems because of a reference to DATA(0). In this case, the **do while** statement in Program 3-2 must be replaced with the equivalent pair of statements

```
do while PTR(I) ≠ 0
    if DATA(PTR(I)) ≥ NAME then exit endif
```

and the one in Program 3-3 with the statements

```
do while PTR(I) ≠ 0
    if DATA(PTR(I)) = NAME then exit endif
```

3.3   MERGING LISTS

Merging is a technique for combining several sorted lists into a single sorted list. It is normally used for combining large files of data held on disk or magnetic tape, but it can be used for combining any kind of sorted list since all that is required is sequential access to the entries in the list. It is a good example of a divide and conquer algorithm when used to sort an unsorted list. We will discuss the *binary* merge, which combines two lists into one, but the merge technique can be used for any number of lists.

FIGURE 3-11 Binary merge

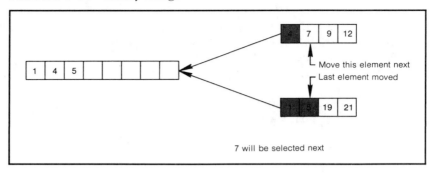

We start by dividing the list into two sublists of approximately equal length. The way this is done depends on the way the lists are stored. In many cases it can be done as they are generated. The two sublists are then sorted by any suitable technique. (How? The beauty of divide and conquer is that we don't care. The sublists are smaller, so the task has to be simpler. If the sublists are of length 1, they are already sorted. If not, we could use the technique we are about to describe or any other.) We combine the two sublists into one using a merge as follows. We compare the first entries on each list and select the smaller (assuming that the lists are sorted into ascending order), which is then moved to the output list (and consequently removed from one of the input lists). This process is repeated with the new first members of each list, as illustrated in Figure 3-11. When one input list has been emptied, the remainder of the second input list is copied to the output list, which is now in sorted order.

In this example we moved entries from one list to another, but if the lists are stored in a chained form, it is necessary only to change pointers.

3.4 STACKS AND QUEUES

Chained lists allow entries to be inserted or deleted at any position. Two very important subclasses of lists are *stacks* and *queues*. A queue is a list with the restriction that entries can be added or removed at either end but not in the middle (the name comes from the British word for a line of people waiting for a service). (Strictly speaking, this is a double-ended queue, or *deque*. A *single-ended queue* permits addition on one end, usually thought of as the *queue head*, and deletion from the other end, the *tail*.) A stack is a list in which addition and deletion are allowed only on one end, usually called the *top* of the stack. These structures are particularly useful, first because they arise naturally in many problems, as

FIGURE 3-12 Stack implemented in an array

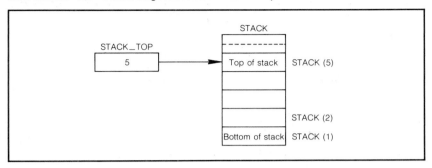

we will see in subsequent chapters, and second because they can be implemented more efficiently than general lists.

Queues arise in situations in which we wish to record information for later use in the order in which it was recorded. As new information is recorded, it is put on the end, or tail, of the queue. When it is used, it is removed from the front, or head, of the queue. For this reason, it is often called a *first-in-first-out* list, or FIFO list. A stack, on the other hand, provides the information in the reverse of the entry order, so it is called a *last-in-first-out*, or LIFO, list. The often-quoted example is the stack of plates in a cafeteria line. Clean plates are added to the top of the stack as available. Customers remove plates from the top. The operation of adding an entry to a stack is called a *push* operation. The operation of removing an entry is called a *pop* operation. The physical analogy with the cafeteria plates is obvious.

When a stack is used to record data, we can visualize it as a stack of storage cells in which a new cell is added to the top of the stack during a push operation and removed during a pop operation. A chained list can be used to implement this visualization. The "new storage cell" for a push operation can be obtained from a free list; after a pop operation a cell must be returned to the free list. However, a stack can be implemented more efficiently using an array. Suppose we know that no more than 150 entries will be present in the stack at any one time.* We can dimension an array STACK to have 150 entries, and assign STACK(1) to hold the bottom entry, STACK(2) to hold the next entry, and so on. The location of the top of the stack must be known, so another integer variable, STACK_TOP, is needed to hold the index of the top of the stack, as shown in Figure 3-12. The operation push onto stack can be coded as

---

*If an attempt occurs to put more entries into a stack than it will hold, we have *stack overflow*. Conversely, *stack underflow* is an attempt to remove an entry from an empty stack.

```
if STACK_TOP < 150
    then
        STACK_TOP ← STACK_TOP + 1
        STACK(STACK_TOP) ← VAR
    else
        output 'STACK OVERFLOW IN PUSH OPERATION'
endif
```

The pop stack to VAR operation can be coded as

```
if STACK_TOP > 0
    then
        VAR ← STACK(STACK_TOP)
        STACK_TOP ← STACK_TOP - 1
    else
        output 'STACK UNDERFLOW IN POP OPERATION'
endif
```

Arrays have several advantages over chained lists for implementing stacks. Less memory space is used, because pointers do not have to be stored. Furthermore, about half as many operations are needed in the push and pop operations when arrays are used. The main disadvantage of arrays is that their size must be fixed before the stack is first used, so it is necessary to know the maximum size of the stack ahead of time.

Arrays can also be used to implement queues. Because data can be added or deleted from either end, the lower end of the queue cannot

FIGURE 3-13 Queue implemented in an array

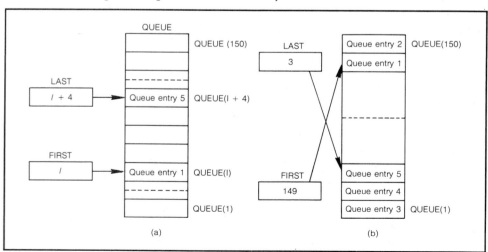

be assumed to be in a fixed place, as in a stack. Consequently, the indices of both ends of the queue must be kept. Figure 3-13a shows an array QUEUE being used to hold a queue whose two ends are in QUEUE (FIRST) and QUEUE(LAST), respectively. If a number of entries are added to the FIRST end, FIRST will be decremented and may eventually go below 1. In this case we must store entries in the top end of the array, as shown in Figure 3-13b, where the queue contains five entries. We can also arrive at the state shown in Figure 3-13b by adding a large number of entries to the LAST end while removing them from the FIRST end; when the LAST end of the queue reaches the top of the array, it must "wrap around" to the lower end of the array.

PROBLEMS

1 Notice that Program 3-3 does not make use of the alphabetical order of the data. This means that if we try to delete a name that is not in the list, we will examine every element in the list looking for it. Change Program 3-3 so that it does not search past the first entry in the list larger than NAME. (This cuts the execution time in half when NAME is not present.)

2 a. Write a subprogram to add a name to the end of an *unordered* list stored in the same way as in Programs 3-1 through 3-4. Your subprogram should take an additional parameter, END, containing the index of the last element in the list.

  b. Modify Program 3-3 to accept a similar parameter END and reset it appropriately if the last element in the list is deleted.

  c. What value should be stored in END when the list is empty? (This value should be chosen to avoid having to test for special cases in the program.)

3 Write a program to sort an unordered chained list, using the bubble sort method given in Chapter 2.

4 Why is it not advisable to use a binary search on an ordered list?

5 An insertion sort cannot be performed on a chained list without some fancy footwork, because the insertion sort scans in both directions: forward to see if anything is out of order, and backward to move an out-of-order item to its proper place. Here is a technique that can be used:

   Search forward, looking for an element that is out of place; at the same time, reverse the pointers so that there is a backward chain through the elements that have already been scanned. This chain can be used when it is necessary to move an element back. When the forward scan has been completed, it would appear that we have to scan back through the chain to reverse the pointers again. However, this can be avoided by sorting the list in the reverse order in the first place, so the chain is left in increasing order at the finish.

   Write a program to perform such a sort. It should start with an unordered list in arrays DATA and PTR, with the list head in PTR(1), and finish with a list in increasing order.

6 Write a subprogram that takes two ordered lists, starting in LIST 1 and LIST 2 (that is, the first element of the first list is in DATA(LIST 1) and PTR(LIST 1)), and returns an ordered list containing the elements of both lists. The result should start in LIST 3. No elements of the array DATA should be changed, only the pointers in PTR.

7 Write a version of Program 3-2 under the assumption that the start of the list is in a variable START (which should be an additional parameter). Note the additional code needed when a list head in the PTR array is not used.

8 Write two subprograms that implement a FIFO queue using an array QUEUE as shown in Figure 3-13. Remember that items can only be added to the LAST end and removed from the FIRST end. Your codes should check for queue overflow or underflow (trying to add another entry when the array is full or to remove an entry when the array is empty). Remember to allow for FIRST to contain a larger index than LAST, as shown in Figure 3-13b.

C H A P T E R

4

Searching
and Sorting
in Trees

■   ■   ■   ■   ■   ■   ■

In Chapter 3 we encountered a data structure called a *chained list*, or *list* for short. The advantage of a list is that elements can be inserted in it or removed from it at any point without having to move large amounts of data in memory. There are many applications in which we want to represent relationships between data items—such as ordering (item *A* is less than item *B*), family relationships (entry *A* is the parent of entry *B*), and connection (point *A* is connected to point *B*), just to name a few examples. An ordering relationship can be described by a list, but other relationships involve more complex information—for example, one parent can have several children, or one point can be connected to many other points.

Often it is necessary to represent the *structure* of the data in the computer, so that the structural relationships can be used in solving the problem. Even when the initial data has very little structure, it may be desirable to provide additional structure during the course of the solution in order to implement a fast method. This chapter examines a very important type of data structure, the tree, and discusses its use in searching and sorting. Other types of data structures are discussed in Part IV.

Lists were introduced as a useful mechanism for maintaining sets of unordered or ordered items that are to be updated by insertions and deletions. If a list is unordered, the only way to search for an item is sequentially; but we saw in Chapter 1 that an ordered array allows us to use the fastest method of searching large sets of data, the *binary search*. Unfortunately, Program 1-3 cannot be used on a chained list, because the program refers to the Ith entry in the list. Finding the Ith entry in a chained list requires a number of operations proportional to I. In a binary search, we go to the middle entry in the table. If this is not the entry sought, we go to the middle of the first or second half of the table, depending on whether the middle entry is larger or smaller than the one sought. This process is diagrammed in Figure 4-1.

The figure suggests that we could use a pointer to tell us where the middle of the table is located and then use two more pointers to tell us where the middle parts of the two halves of the table are located. If, after going to the middle of one half of the table, we find that the entry there is not the desired one, we wish to continue to the middle of a half of the half. Again, we could find that entry if we had two more pointers. This

FIGURE 4-1 Binary search

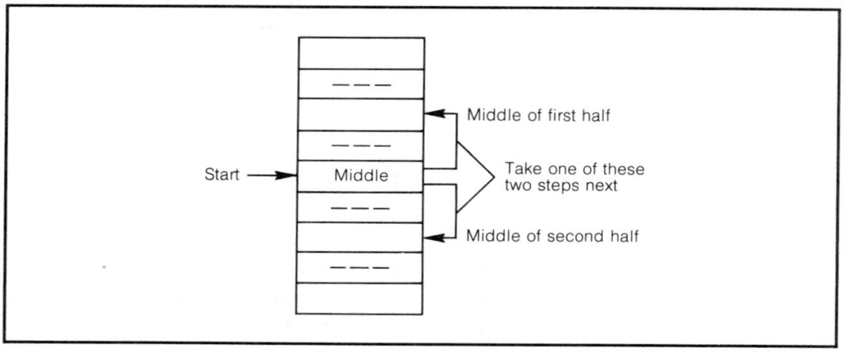

FIGURE 4-2 Search with pointers

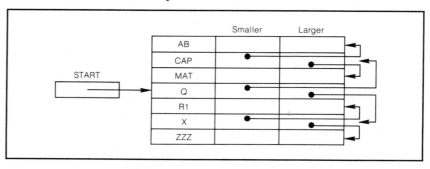

FIGURE 4-3 Expansion of Figure 4-2

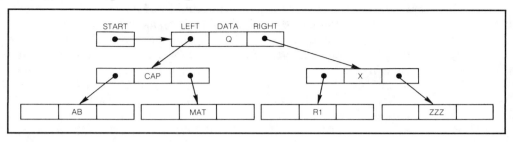

FIGURE 4-4 Tree

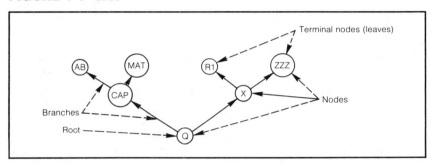

idea is illustrated in Figure 4-2 for a table with seven entries in alphabetical order. Null pointers have been omitted for clarity. Each entry now consists of three items: the data and two pointers, one to the earlier part of the table and one to the later part. The structure becomes clearer if drawn as in Figure 4-3. Each entry is shown as a triplet `LEFT`, `DATA`, and `RIGHT`. `LEFT` is a pointer to the part of the table to the left of the entry, `RIGHT` a pointer to the part of the table to the right of the entry. This type of data structure is called a *tree*. If it is drawn "up the other way," as shown in Figure 4-4, the analogy is obvious, but we will normally draw trees as in Figure 4-3.

Much of the terminology of tree structures is based on horticulture. As shown in Figure 4-4, the bottom (top in Figure 4-3) of a tree is called the *root*, the places where we have entries are called *nodes*, the pointers from one node to other nodes are called *branches*, and the nodes with no pointers leaving them are called *terminal nodes* or *leaves*. Formally, a tree is a set of nodes connected by branches in such a way that there is one and only one way of going from one node to another via branch connections, and which has a distinguished node called the *root node*.

Another part of tree terminology is derived from genealogical trees. The nodes below and directly connected to a given node are called the *offspring* of that node (also called *subnodes*) (see Figure 4-3). Thus `CAP` and X are offspring, or subnodes, of Q. If we start with CAP in Figure 4-3 and consider the part of the tree connected to CAP and not above it, we have another tree, called a *subtree* of the original tree. In this case, the subtree consists of CAP, AB, and MAT. The nodes in the subtree are all *successors*, or *descendants*, of Q. If a node A has a node above it and directly connected to it, say node B, then B is the *parent* of A. The only node without a parent is the root node. If two nodes have the same parent, they are said to be *siblings*. For example, AB and MAT in Figure 4-3 are siblings.

The tree in Figure 4-3 is a special type of tree called a *binary tree*, in which each node has exactly two offspring, referred to as the *left* and *right offspring*. Either or both offspring of a given node may be null. A binary tree is not simply a tree that has no more than two subnodes for any given node. For example, a family tree showing maternal relationships in which no mother has more than two children is not a binary tree, because in the case of a mother with only one child there is no distinction between "left" and "right." In binary trees, this distinction is important. If, for example, the entry ZZZ is removed from Figure 4-3, node X has a null right offspring. The tree is *ordered*, and this property would be destroyed if the subnode R1 were moved from the left to the right of X.

Binary trees are particularly important in computer applications because they are easy to represent using three arrays. The important property of the tree in Figure 4-3 is that all nodes connected via the left pointer of a given node are alphabetically less than that node. Similarly, all nodes connected via the right pointer are alphabetically greater. If we wish to search for a given item, say R1, we start at the root and compare R1 with the entry there. Since R1 is larger, it is either not in the tree or is connected to the right pointer. Therefore we proceed through the right pointer of the root. There we find that R1 is less than the entry X. We therefore proceed via the left pointer and arrive at R1.

Example 4-1
Searching an Ordered Binary Tree

Searching an ordered binary tree can be programmed very simply. The code is shown in Program 4-1. This code is much simpler than that in Program 1-3, because there is no need to construct addresses for the array entries: they are given directly in the pointer arrays LEFT and RIGHT. The program assumes that DATA is an array of integers, but it can be used for any data type by changing the declarations for DATA and X. The variable ROOT contains the index of the root of the tree. Although the table in the example above is "balanced," it is not necessary that the root node contain exactly the middle entry or that any node contain the middle entry of the section of the tree below it (that is, the *subtrees* connected to it via its left and right pointers). But all entries accessible via the left pointer of any node must be alphabetically less than the entry in the node, and all

■ **Program 4.1** **Search ordered binary tree**

```
BINARY_TREE_SEARCH: subprogram (I,DATA,LEFT,
RIGHT,ROOT,X,N)
    This subroutine searches the tree rooted in ROOT. The triplets
    representing the tree are stored in LEFT(J), DATA(J),
    RIGHT(J). If a J is found such that DATA(J) = X, I is set to
    J; otherwise I is set to 0.
    integer I,N,DATA(N),LEFT(N),RIGHT(N),ROOT,X
        I ← ROOT
        do while I ≠ 0 and DATA(I) ≠ X
            if DATA(I) > X
                then I ← LEFT(I)
                else I ← RIGHT(I)
                endif
            enddo
    return
endsubprogram BINARY_TREE_SEARCH
```

entries accessible via the right pointer must be alphabetically greater: that is, the tree must be *ordered*. If this relationship is maintained, then the search algorithm given in Program 4-1 will work.

As an example, the data given in Figure 4-3 could be stored using the tree structure shown in Figure 4-5. The tree is still ordered, so that when we search for R1, we can compare it with MAT in the root node and determine that it must lie in the subtree to the right of that node if it is in the table. The difference between Figures 4-3 and 4-5 is only one of average execution time. Suppose each of the seven entries were to be looked

FIGURE 4-5 Alternative tree for storing data in Figure 4-3

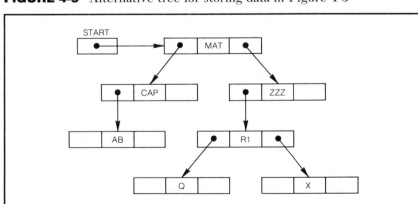

TABLE 4-1 Levels of search necessary

Entry	Levels of Search		
	Balanced Tree in Figure 4-3	Unbalanced Tree in Figure 4-5	Worst-Case Tree in Figure 4-6
AB	3	3	1
CAP	2	2	3
MAT	3	1	4
Q	1	4	7
R1	3	3	6
X	2	4	5
ZZZ	3	2	2
Total	17	19	28
Average	2.43	2.71	4.00

up. The number of levels of the tree that must be searched is shown in Table 4-1. We can see that a balanced tree leads to fewer operations on the average if any item is equally likely to be referenced. The extreme case occurs when all nodes have a null subtree on one side, as shown in Figure 4-6. The number of levels of search necessary for this case is also given in Table 4-1. The tree in Figure 4-6 is equivalent to a list, since there is only one branch from each node. Consequently, a search in this tree is equivalent to a sequential search: we expect the average time to be about $N/2$, where N is the number of entries.

Because a binary tree does not have to remain balanced, it is easy to add a new entry. Suppose we have the configuration shown in Figure 4-5 and we wish to add the string CAR. We search down the table looking for CAR until we reach a null pointer. If we were to find CAR, we couldn't add it, because our structure does not allow for repeated entries. In this example we find a null pointer when we attempt to go right from CAP, so we add CAR to the tree at that point. This occurs as a result of the following sequence of steps:

1. Compare CAR with MAT. CAR is less, so go left.
2. Compare CAR with CAP. CAR is greater, so go right.
3. Right contains a null pointer, so stop and put CAR on the right of CAP.

Successive stages starting from an empty table and adding the strings CAN, AC, MAT, Z1, and I3 are shown in Figure 4-7.

FIGURE 4-6 Worst-case tree for data in Figure 4-3

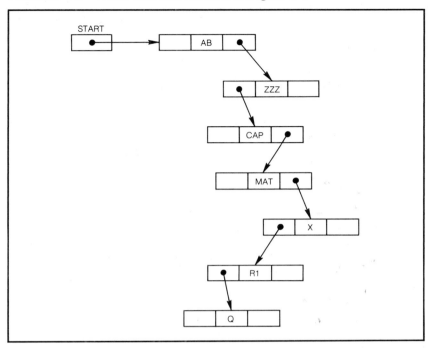

As new items are added to a tree, storage space for the triplets can be obtained from a storage-allocation mechanism using a free list (in this case a list of triplets). If items are to be deleted from a tree, the space freed can then be returned to the free list.

Deletion from an ordered tree is more difficult. Unless the deleted entry is a terminal node, some reorganization of pointers is necessary. If either the right or the left pointer of the deleted entry is null, the problem can be handled as in a list (see Figure 4-8). In all other cases we must replace the deleted entry with an entry from either its left or its right subtree. Suppose we decide to use an entry from the right subtree. It must be the smallest entry in that subtree, as shown in Figure 4-9.

Program 4-2 performs the operation shown in Figure 4-9. This example is worth studying, because it illustrates the importance of selecting the proper representation for the data structure. When we try to program deletion, we find that special cases complicate the program and make it difficult to follow. Suppose we start by trying to write a subprogram to remove the node with index I. It is clear that the contents of the parent node of I must be modified: if we do not give the index of the parent as a parameter, the entire tree must be searched to find the parent. (If we are given the *data* to be removed, a search for the node containing that data will also

FIGURE 4-7 Successive stages of tree building

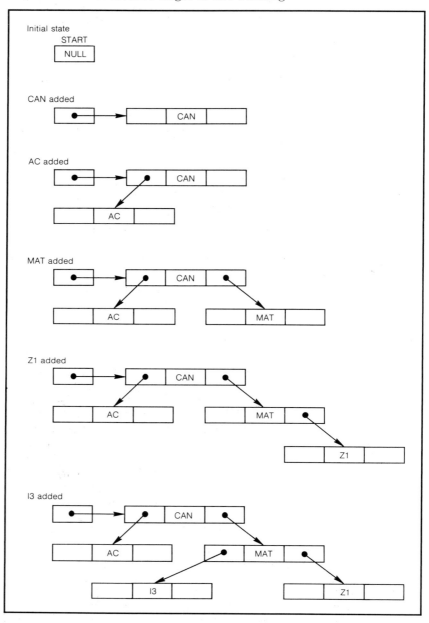

FIGURE 4·8 Deletion from an ordered tree

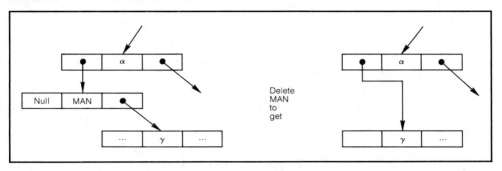

FIGURE 4·9 Deletion when replacement necessary

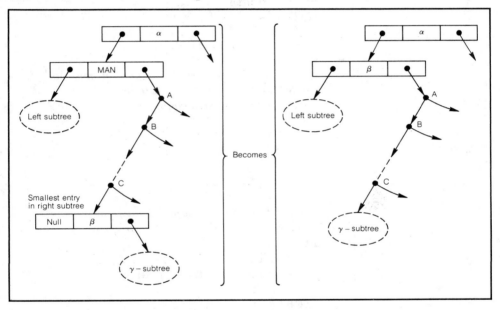

find the parent.) If the item to be removed is the root node, there is an immediately obvious special case: there is no parent. This special case can be eliminated by storing the index of the root in one of the pointer variables, say LEFT(1), making it appear that the root has a parent at index 1.

Because the node to be removed may be either the left or the right offspring of the parent, it is necessary to indicate which. Program 4-2 requires that this be done by using a negative pointer value if the node to be removed is the left subnode, and a positive pointer value otherwise.

■ Program 4.2   Delete a node from a binary tree

```
DELETE_NODE: subprogram (I,LEFT,RIGHT,N)
```
The node that is the offspring of the node at index ABS(I) *is removed from the binary tree with pointers stored in arrays* LEFT *and* RIGHT. *If* I *is negative, the left offspring is to be removed, otherwise the right is to be removed.*
```
    integer I,N,LEFT(N),RIGHT(N),J,K,L
```
J is set to the index of the node to be removed, L *to the index of the node to be put in its place—that is,* I *will point to* L *instead of* J *at completion.*
```
    if I < 0 then J ← LEFT(-I) else J ← RIGHT(I)
        endif
    if LEFT(J) = 0 or RIGHT(J) = 0
        then
```
If either subtree of J *is null, remove* J *immediately as in Figure 4-8.*
```
            L ← LEFT(J) + RIGHT(J)
        else
```
Go down right subtree of J *to find leftmost node* L *(node β in Figure 4-9). Set* K *to point to parent of node* L *with same sign convention as used for* I.
```
            K ← J
            L ← RIGHT(J)
            do while LEFT(L) ≠ 0
                K ← - L
                L ← LEFT(L)
                enddo
```
Move L *to position occupied by* J *by replacing pointers in* L. *Make* K *point to offspring of* L.
```
            if K < 0
                then LEFT(- K) ← RIGHT(L)
                else RIGHT(K) ← RIGHT(L)
                endif
            RIGHT(L) ← RIGHT(J)
            LEFT(L) ← LEFT(J)
        endif
```
Finally, make I *point to* L.
```
    if I < 0 then LEFT(-I) ← L else RIGHT(I) ← L
        endif
    return
endsubprogram DELETE_NODE
```

4.1 TRAVERSING TREES

We often wish to visit all nodes of a tree in some special order. In the case of an ordered binary tree, we may want to visit each node in its natural ordering, to print it. Let us consider the tree in Figure 4-10: a, b, and c are the addresses of locations in which the tree elements are stored (or are their indices in an array used for storage). We start at the node containing B, but before we can print that, we must print all entries in the subtree to the left of B. Therefore we move left to A. Since that has no subtree to its left, we can print A. Now, since there is no subtree to the right of A, we must move back to B and print it. But how can we get back to B? We have no pointer to show us the way back. When we moved down to A from B, we should have saved the address b of B.

Now consider the tree in Figure 4-11. We move left to A2 from B, saving its address, b. There is a subtree to the left of A2, so we must print that subtree before printing A2. Hence we move left from A2, saving its address, $a2$. As we go deeper into the tree, we will accumulate more and more addresses that must be saved so that we can find our way back. How should we save these addresses? A stack structure is exactly what we want, because when we return up the tree, we will want to revisit all nodes in reverse order. Each time we go deeper into the tree, we put the

FIGURE 4-10 Tree with three entries

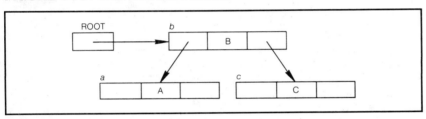

FIGURE 4-11 Tree with five entries

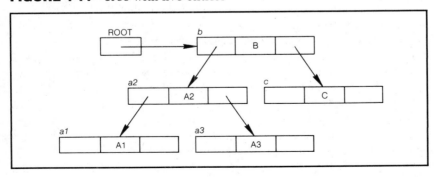

FIGURE 4-12   Stack with two entries

Top level	a2
Bottom level	b

■ **Program 4.3   Print an ordered binary tree**

```
PRINT_TREE: subprogram (ROOT,LEFT,DATA,RIGHT,N)
   integer ROOT,N,LEFT(N),DATA(N),RIGHT(N),PTR
   The tree rooted at ROOT is printed in order. A stack keeps track of
   the path into the tree.
      PTR ← ROOT
      set stack empty
      do while PTR ≠ 0 or stack not empty
         GO_LEFT: do while PTR ≠0
            This loop goes down to the left until a NULL pointer
            is found.
            push PTR onto stack
            PTR ← LEFT(PTR)
            enddo GO_LEFT
         pop stack to PTR
         output DATA(PTR)
         PTR ← RIGHT(PTR)
         enddo
      return
   endsubprogram PRINT_TREE
```

address of the entry we are leaving on top of the stack. When, for example, we have reached A1 in Figure 4-11, the stack will be as shown in Figure 4-12. When we wish to return to the next higher level, A2, its address is on top of the stack. After we remove it, the address of the level above, B, is on top of the stack.

Suppose we have just printed A1. We return to the next higher level by removing the address a2 from the top of the stack. Now we can print A2. Next we wish to go to the right subtree of A2 and print it. What should we save in the stack in order to return? After we have printed the right subtree, we do not wish to return to A2, because we have already printed it. Instead, we wish to go straight to B and print it. Thus when we go down to the right of A2 we need not put a return into the stack. The address b already there is the appropriate place to which to return.

Program 4-3 prints an ordered binary tree rooted in ROOT in increasing order. It uses the push and pop operations, written as push X onto stack and pop stack into X. The latter functions as an assignment statement, changing the value of X; the former simply copies the value of X onto the top of the stack. The binary tree is assumed to be stored in LEFT, DATA, and RIGHT as before.

4.2 USE OF RECURSION

In the previous section we used a stack to remember the path we had taken down into the tree from the root. When a language permits recursion, it remembers the path by which we have arrived at a particular invocation of a subprogram, so the recursive mechanism can be used to trace through a tree. However, if we *think* recursively, the design of an algorithm to handle tasks such as tree traversal is extremely simple. Recursion is the direct application of the idea of divide and conquer. In a recursive program, we subdivide the problem into simpler cases, and then apply the same method to the simpler cases by calling the same program to handle them. Since the process must stop somewhere, a recursive program must detect the simplest case and handle it directly. (If the subdivision does not eventually terminate in a simple case that can be handled directly, recursion cannot be used.)

In the tree-printing example, a recursive program to print an ordered tree will simply print the left subtree of the root, then print the value at the root, and finally print the right subtree of the root. How does it print the subtrees? It uses the same mechanism and divides the subtrees into

■ **Program 4.3a**   **Print an ordered binary tree**

```
PRINT_TREE: subprogram (ROOT,LEFT,DATA,RIGHT,N)
    The binary tree rooted in ROOT is printed recursively in ascending
    order.
    integer ROOT,N,LEFT(N),DATA(N),RIGHT(N)
        If ROOT is null, do nothing but return; otherwise print the left
        subtree, followed by the data at the root, and the right
        subtree.
        if ROOT ≠ 0
            then
                call PRINT_TREE(LEFT(ROOT),LEFT,
                  DATA,RIGHT,N)
                output DATA(ROOT)
                call PRINT_TREE(RIGHT(ROOT),LEFT,
                  DATA,RIGHT,N)
            endif
        return
    endsubprogram PRINT_TREE
```

sub-subtrees. What is the simplest case? A null tree, which requires nothing to be printed. Program 4-3a is a modification of Program 4-3 to print an ordered tree using recursion. Note that it has a much simpler structure than Program 4-3.

PROBLEMS

1 What is the maximum number of entries that can be stored in a binary tree if the longest path from the root to any node does not exceed n? What is the average search time for any entry in that tree when n is 3, 4, or 5? Can you give the average for any n?

2 If Program 4-3a is used to print the tree shown in Figure 4-3, what is the sequence of calls on PRINT_TREE? (Give the value of the parameter ROOT for each call.)

3 Write a recursive program to search for an entry X in an ordered binary tree.

4 Suppose you have to write a program to input a set of words and their definitions. (Each word and its definition can be viewed as a character string.) The program must also accept words without definitions as input, in which case it is to print the definition of the word if one was previously input. Finally, the program is to output a list of all words input in alphabetical order with definitions. Would you use a binary tree to order the words alphabetically, or one of the sorting methods discussed in previous chapters? Consider two different cases: (1) all the words with definitions are input before any of the words without definitions; (2) the definitions and the words to be looked up can appear in the input in any order.

II

APPROXIMATION OF KNOWN AND UNKNOWN FUNCTIONS

■   ■   ■   ■

Engineering, scientific, and economic calculations often require the evaluation of various functions. These may be well-known mathematical functions, such as sine and exponential, or they may be functions peculiar to the problem, such as the force needed to stretch a particular type of material a given amount. The first examples above are known functions in the sense that they are mathematically defined. It may, however, be difficult to compute them, so we will have to be content with an approximation. The second example above is an unknown function in that we cannot determine anything except some sample values of the function by experiment. In an engineering design problem we may need to "guess" at other values of the function. For example, suppose we have measured the stretching (strain) of a metal bar for various amounts of applied force (stress), and have obtained the values shown in Figure II-1. We might want to know the strain for values of the stress that we haven't tried. If we assume that a smooth curve can be drawn connecting the measured points, as in Figure II-1, we can obtain the desired values from that curve. If this information is to be used in a computer program (for example, to calculate whether a proposed design for

FIGURE II-1   Measured values of a function

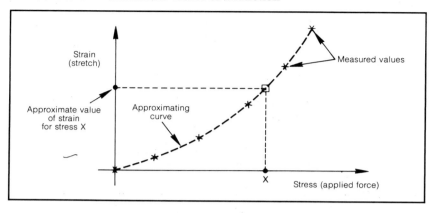

a bridge will stand up to intended usage), we would like to store the observed values in the computer and use them to calculate an approximation to the strain for any applied stress. This example is also complicated by the fact that the values we measure experimentally are likely to contain small errors. We might therefore consider taking a large number of measurements in the hope of "averaging out the error."

In this part of the book we will consider a number of ways of approximating functions of both types. Most of these methods can be used for either type of function, but each is more naturally suited to one type.

C H A P T E R

5

Series
Methods

■　　　■　　　■　　　■　　　■　　　■

Scientists and engineers use many functions in their work, such as square root, sine, and cosine, that are not basic operations on a computer and cannot be expressed in a finite number of basic operations. However, they can be approximated to any desired precision using basic operations. Many of these functions can be described by means of *power series*. For example, we can write

$$\exp(x) = 1 + x + \frac{x^2}{2!} + \frac{x^3}{3!} + \cdots$$

$$\log(1 + x) = x - \frac{x^2}{2} + \frac{x^3}{3} - \frac{x^4}{4} + \cdots \qquad (\text{for } |x| < 1)$$

$$\sin(x) = x - \frac{x^3}{3!} + \frac{x^5}{5!} - \cdots$$

$$\cos(x) = 1 - \frac{x^2}{2!} + \frac{x^4}{4!} - \cdots$$

In principle, we can substitute the value of x into these power series and approximate the value of the function as closely as we like by computing a sufficient number of terms; but there are some difficulties, both theoretical and practical. Some series are valid only for restricted ranges of the argument x. The logarithm (log) function, for example, has no meaning if the absolute value of x is not less than 1. (We can see this by considering the behavior of the series when, say, $x = 2$: the terms increase without bound. We say that the infinite sum *does not converge.*)

Even if the series is valid for all values of x, it may be possible to achieve greater precision with fewer terms when x is small. For example, if we evaluate exp(10.0) by substituting $x = 10.0$ into the series above, we find that we have to compute 25 terms to get four significant digits of precision. By comparison, if we evaluate exp(0.1), we can achieve four significant digits in just four terms. Consequently, we should never blindly evaluate the terms in the power series as they stand, but should look for ways to take advantage of the properties of the series. The standard technique is *argument reduction*, which attempts to reduce the argument to a small value. We will illustrate with several examples.

The series for the log function is valid only for a restricted range of argument values, so it is essential to reduce the argument to within this range. We can use the properties of logarithms to achieve this. Suppose the argument z is expressed as $z = f \times 10^e$, where $0.1 \le f < 1.0$—that is, we have a decimal floating-point representation of the strictly positive number z. (The argument to the log function cannot be zero or negative, because the logarithm does not then exist in real arithmetic.) By the properties of logarithms, we can write

$$\log(z) = \log(f \times 10^e) = \log(f) + \log(10^e)$$
$$= \log(1 + (f - 1)) + e \times \log(10)$$

Since $\log(10)$ is a constant, we can evaluate $e \times \log(10)$ with a multiplication. Since $x = (f - 1)$ is between -0.9 and 0.0, we can approximate $\log(1 + (f - 1)) = \log(1 + x)$ by using the series above.

On computers that use binary floating point, we can simply substitute 2 for 10 in the discussion above. In fact, we can do this even on a computer that uses some other form of number representation. To compute the logarithm of a number z, we first find an integer n such that

$$2^{n-1} \le z < 2^n$$

Then we write

$$\log(z) = \log(2^{-n}z \times 2^n) = \log(1 + (2^{-n}z - 1)) + n \log(2)$$

Now the argument to be used in the series expansion of the log function is $x = 2^{-n}z - 1$, which is between -0.5 and 0.0. When an argument of -0.5

is used in the expansion, only 10 terms are needed to achieve four-digit precision, compared with nearly 60 terms when the argument is -0.9.

The argument of the exponential function can be reduced in a similar manner. Suppose that $z = n + f$, where n is an integer and f lies between -0.5 and $+0.5$. Then we can write

$$\exp(z) = \exp(n + f) = \exp(n) \times \exp(f)$$

The first term, $\exp(n)$, can be computed entirely with multiplications if n is positive, or with multiplications and one division if n is negative. The second term can be computed using the power-series approximation. Since the magnitude of the argument does not exceed 0.5, relatively few terms are needed. For example, four significant digits can be obtained with no more than six terms.

The arguments of the sine and cosine functions can be reduced by using their periodicity properties—that is, the fact that

$$\sin(x) = \sin(x + 2\pi n)$$
$$\cos(x) = \cos(x + 2\pi n)$$

for any integer n. (A *periodic function* with *period T* is a function f such that $f(x) = f(x + T)$ for all values of x. The period of the sine and cosine functions is 2π.) We can use this property to reduce any argument z to within the range 0 to 2π by writing

$$\sin(z) = \sin(z - 2\pi n)$$

where n is chosen so that $z - 2\pi n$ falls within the desired range. We can simplify the problem still further by using the relations

$$\sin(x - \pi) = -\sin(x)$$

$$\sin\left(x + \frac{\pi}{2}\right) = \cos(x)$$

The graph of $\sin(x)$ for x between 0 and 2π is shown in Figure 5-1. It is broken up into sections using the relationships above, so that we can use either the sine or the cosine series in the regions shown. For example, if x is between $5\pi/4$ and $7\pi/4$, we compute

$$\sin(x) = -\cos(x - 3\pi/2)$$

so that the argument of the cosine function satisfies

$$-\pi/4 \le x - 3\pi/2 \le \pi/4$$

FIGURE 5-1   Calculation of sin(x)

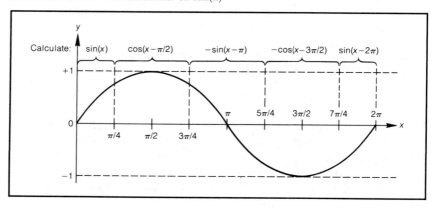

In this way the argument used in the series expansion is always between $-\pi/4$ and $+\pi/4$.

Because we now know that $|x| \le \pi/4 \cong 0.7854$, we can decide how many terms we need in the sine and cosine series. Suppose we want four decimal digits of precision—that is, we want

$$\left| \frac{\text{error in calculated } \sin(x)}{\sin(x)} \right| \le 10^{-4}$$

It is known that $|\sin(x)| \ge \dfrac{2}{\pi} x$ for all $|x| \le \dfrac{\pi}{2}$;* hence we ask that the sum of the neglected terms be less than $10^{-4} |x| \dfrac{2}{\pi}$. The series for $\sin(x)$ is an example of an *alternating series*—that is, the terms alternate in sign. Further, when $|x| < 1$, the terms decrease in magnitude. If we were to approximate $\sin(x)$ by powers up to x^5, the error would consist of the sum of those terms in parentheses in the series

$$\sin(x) = x - \frac{x^3}{3!} + \frac{x^5}{5!} - \left(\frac{x^7}{7!} - \frac{x^9}{9!} \right) - \left(\frac{x^{11}}{11!} - \frac{x^{13}}{13!} \right) - \cdots$$

The expressions in parentheses have the same sign as x, since $|x| < 1$. Hence the sum of the first three terms of the sine series gives a result whose error has the same sign as x—that is, the approximation is larger

---

*We can see this by drawing a straight line between the origin and the first peak of the sine curve (at $x = \pi/2$, $y = 1$) in Figure 5-1. This line, which has the equation $y = \dfrac{2}{\pi} x$, is below the sine curve for all values of x between 0.0 and $\pi/2$.

than sin(x) if x is positive and smaller than sin(x) if x is negative. We can also write

$$\sin(x) = x - \frac{x^3}{3!} + \frac{x^5}{5!} - \frac{x^7}{7!} + \left(\frac{x^9}{9!} - \frac{x^{11}}{11!}\right) + \left(\frac{x^{13}}{13!} - \frac{x^{15}}{15!}\right) + \cdots$$

This time the error in using the first three terms is seen to be $-x^7/7!$ plus a series of terms that have the same sign as x. Thus the error in using the first three terms is between zero and $x^7/7!$. This is a particular instance of a general result for all alternating series of decreasing terms: *the magnitude of the error is no larger than the first neglected term.* Consequently we can decide how many terms of the sine series to use by finding the smallest n for which the relation

$$\left| \frac{x^{2n+1}}{(2n+1)!} \right| < 10^{-4} |x| \frac{2}{\pi}$$

holds when $|x| \leq 0.7854$. This can be done by computing $(0.7854)^{2n}/(2n+1)!$ for $n = 1, 2, \ldots$ until we get a result less than $10^{-4} \frac{2}{\pi} \cong 0.000064$. The values are shown in Table 5-1, from which we see that use of the first three terms of the sine series gives the desired precision.

To get four significant digits from the cosine series, we can again use the alternating property of the series. For $|x| \leq \pi/4$, $\cos(x) > 1/\sqrt{2} \cong 0.7071$. Hence we want the first neglected term to be less than 0.7071×10^{-4}. This time, therefore, we want to find an n such that $(0.7854)^{2n}/(2n)! < 0.7071 \times 10^{-4}$. Table 5-2 shows that an n of 4 is adequate. Therefore, for $|x| \leq \pi/4$, $\cos(x)$ can be approximated by

TABLE 5-1 Maximum Error for Sine

n	1	2	3	4
$\dfrac{(0.7854)^{2n}}{(2n+1)!}$	0.1028089	0.0031709	0.0000466	0.0000004

TABLE 5-2 Maximum Error for Cosine

n	1	2	3	4
$\dfrac{(0.7854)^{2n}}{(2n)!}$	0.3084266	0.0158545	0.0003260	0.0000036

$$1 - \frac{x^2}{2!} + \frac{x^4}{4!} - \frac{x^6}{6!}$$

to four significant digits.

Program 5-1 illustrates the steps in the argument reduction. It first determines the number of multiples of 2π that can be subtracted from the input argument X. (In fact, it subtracts multiples of π. If an even number of multiples are subtracted, the result is not changed. If an odd number are subtracted, the sign of the result is reversed.) Program 5-1 calls on two auxiliary functions, SIN 1 and COS 1, which compute the sine and cosine using the power series, under the assumption that their arguments are no more than $\pi/4$. These functions could be written out in the obvious way, but there are some efficiency considerations, which will be taken up in the next section. Program 5-1 declares some *constants* by giving their equivalent value in the declaration statement; for example, **real** PI = 3.14159. This facility is available directly in some languages, such as Pascal. In others, it must be done by assignment statements.

Program 5-1 is *not* representative of the way the built-in functions SIN and COS are actually coded. Those functions are used very frequently, so it is important that they be made as efficient as possible. Normally they are written in machine language, to take advantage of every quirk of the computer, and to use additional techniques to reduce the argument and hence the amount of arithmetic needed. However, Program 5-1 does illustrate the type of idea used.

■ **Program 5.1   Argument reduction for sine computation**

```
SIN: subprogram (X)
     This function computes the sine of the argument X, which is given
     in radians. X is reduced until it is in the range 0.0 to π/4, and is
     then passed on to one of the auxiliary functions SIN 1 or COS 1.
     real SIN,X,X1,Z,PI = 3.14159,PIBY2 = 1.57080,
          PIBY4 = 0.78540
     integer N
          N ← X/PI
          X1 ← X - N*PI
          if X1 > PIBY2 then X1 ← PI - X1 endif
          if X1 < PIBY4
               then Z ← SIN 1(X1)
               else Z ← COS 1(PIBY2 - X1)
               endif
          if N ≠ (N ÷ 2)*2 then Z ← -Z endif
          return (Z)
     endsubprogram SIN
```

5.1 HORNER'S METHOD

We have seen that a number of functions can be expressed approximately as polynomials. We now turn to the problem of efficiently evaluating a polynomial.

The obvious way of writing an expression for a polynomial of *degree n* implies the use of $n(n+1)/2$ multiplications. For example, the cubic (degree-3) polynomial $a_0 + a_1x + a_2x^2 + a_3x^3$ implies six multiplications. This can be seen if the multiplications are indicated explicitly:

$$p(x) = a_0 + a_1x + a_2xx + a_3xxx$$

We can save one multiplication by forming x^3 as the product of x and x^2, which we have already calculated. In this way we can calculate a polynomial of degree n with only $2n - 1$ multiplications, by writing it in the form

$$p(x) = a_0 + a_1x + a_2x_2 + a_3x_3 + \cdots + a_nx_n$$
$$(n \text{ multiplications})$$

where

$$\left.\begin{aligned} x_2 &= x^2 \\ x_3 &= x_2x \\ &\;\;\vdots \\ x_n &= x_{n-1}x \end{aligned}\right\} \quad (n - 1 \text{ multiplications})$$

This calculation could be programmed using a loop. However, the number of multiplications can be reduced still further—to a total of n— by factoring the polynomial. The cubic example given above can be written as

$$p(x) = a_0 + x(a_1 + x(a_2 + xa_3))$$

which takes only three multiplications (and no more additions than the previous methods). This form of factorization is known as Horner's method, and it can be shown that it is not possible, in the general case of arbitrary coefficients a_i, to reduce the number of multiplications or additions further.

If a low-degree polynomial is to be evaluated, a single expression can be written using this factored form; but if the polynomial is of high degree, it is simpler to use a loop. Program 5-2 gives a function subprogram to evaluate a polynomial of degree N whose Ith coefficient is in location `A(I + 1)`. Notice that the loop starts with the Nth coefficient, in location `A(N + 1)`, and works backward to the lowest-degree term. This is indicated with the "`by -1`" construction.

■ **Program 5.2   Evaluate polynomial by Horner's method**

```
POLYNOMIAL: subprogram (A,N,X)
```
   Function to compute the value of the polynomial
$$A(1) + A(2)*X + \cdots + A(N + 1)*X \uparrow N$$
   using only N multiplications.
```
   integer I,N
   real POLYNOMIAL,A(N + 1),P,X
       P ← A(N + 1)
       do for I ← N to 1 by -1
        P ← P*X + A(I)
          enddo
       return (P)
   endsubprogram POLYNOMIAL
```

■ **Program 5.3   Compute cosine by power series**

```
COS: subprogram (X)
```
   Array C contains the coefficients for the first seven terms in the
   power series: $1/0!$, $1/2!$, $1/4!$, $1/6!$, $1/8!$, $1/10!$, *and*
   $1/12!$.
```
   real C(7) = (1.0,0.5,0.41667E - 1,0.13889E - 2,
   0.24802E - 4,0.27557E - 6,0.20877E - 8)
   real X,Y,P,COS
   integer I
       P ← C(7)
       Y ← -X*X
       do for I ← 6 to 1 by -1
           P ← P*Y + C(I)
          enddo
       return (P)
   endsubprogram COS
```

If some of the powers of x are missing from the polynomial, it may be possible to improve the speed of the program. The power-series approximation to the cosine function, for example, includes only even powers of x. We can approximate the cosine by using the first seven terms in the form of an expression:

$$1 + y\left(-\frac{1}{2!} + y\left(\frac{1}{4!} + y\left(-\frac{1}{6!} + y\left(\frac{1}{8!} + y\left(-\frac{1}{10!} + y\left(\frac{1}{12!}\right)\right)\right)\right)\right)\right)$$

where $y = x^2$.

Program 5-3 performs the same computation using a loop instead of a single expression. If the function $COS(X)$ were not provided in a language, we could define it by writing a function subprogram like the one shown. Notice that this program uses an initial-value declaration to initialize the array C. The seven values given in parentheses in the declaration statement, following the equal sign, will be placed into the seven locations in array C when the program is first loaded into memory. Since the elements of C are not changed during execution, they will have these values whenever the subprogram is used. Program 5-3 shows the magnitudes of the coefficients in C. Since the coefficients have alternating signs, the signs are handled by setting Y to $-X^2$.

PROBLEMS

1 Write a program to evaluate $\sin(x)$, using the power series without argument reduction and stopping when the next term is less than 10^{-6}. Run this program for $x = \pi/4, 9\pi/4, 17\pi/4, \ldots , (4n + 1)\pi/4$. Print the answer and the number of terms needed to achieve the required precision. Do you notice anything interesting in addition to the increased number of terms needed?

2 Write a program to compute $\exp(z)$, using argument reduction to get an argument in the range -0.5 to $+0.5$. Use an array $E(I)$, containing $\exp(I)$ for I from 1 to 50, to assist in the computation. Assume that z does not exceed 50 in magnitude, and that four significant figures are needed in the answer.

6

Interpolation

■   ■   ■   ■   ■   ■   ■

Interpolation refers to the computation of an approximate value of a function by use of its values at nearby points. Interpolation is the approach to use when we are given very accurate values of experimental data at a number of points and wish to approximate the corresponding function at any intermediate point. For example, airplane designs are tested on computers to determine whether they will fly at various speeds and attitudes. The flight of the plane is simulated by computing all the forces on it. (This sort of simulation will be discussed in Chapter 20.) The data for the drag (the slowing force due to air resistance) and lift (the forces on the wings that hold the plane up in the air) is obtained from wind-tunnel tests of models (or possibly full-size structures) of the wings and other parts of the plane. This data is obtained for a number of different airspeeds and different settings of the control flaps on the wing, etc. During the simulation, the forces on the wing must be calculated for whatever speed the simulated plane has. The forces are approximated by interpolating from the values obtained experimentally.

We may also use interpolation to approximate a function when the computation of that function is possible but extremely slow. In that case, it might be more efficient to compute the function for several different values of its argument once and for all and to approximate the function value by interpolation from those values each time it must be computed. If the cost of interpolation is much less than the cost of computing the function, and if the function has to be approximated a very large number of times, a considerable amount of computer time can be saved.

Linear interpolation consists of approximating the function by a straight line between any pair of adjacent points at which the function is known, as shown between the points P and Q in Figure 6-1. Suppose we are given a set of argument values, $x(i)$, and the corresponding function values, $y(i)$, in a table held in a pair of arrays, X and Y. If the argument values satisfy

$$x(i) < x(i + 1)$$

for all i between 1 and $n - 1$ (n is the number of entries in the table), and if we connect each pair of consecutive points with a straight line, we get an approximation to the curve of the function such as that shown in Figure 6-2.

To approximate the value of the function for an x value not in the table, we must make a calculation based on the geometry shown in Figure 6-1. First we must find the pair of consecutive x values, $x(i)$ and $x(i + 1)$, that surround the desired point x. Then we can compute the value y of the corresponding point on the straight line PQ as

$$y = y(i) + d$$

$$= y(i) + [y(i + 1) - y(i)]\,\frac{x - x(i)}{x(i + 1) - x(i)}$$

FIGURE 6-1   Computing the linear approximant

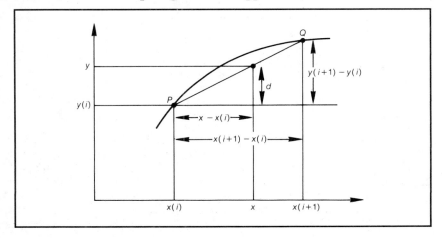

FIGURE 6-2   Linear interpolation

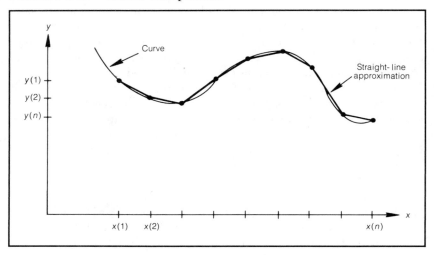

There are two different cases to consider: equal and unequal spacing. If the points x are equally spaced—that is, if

$$x(2) - x(1) = x(3) - x(2) = \cdots = x(n) - x(n - 1)$$

then we do not have to store the values of $x(i)$: if we call the common spacing

$$h = x(2) - x(1) = x(i + 1) - x(i)$$

and define

$$x_0 = x(1) - h$$

then we can compute $x(i)$ from the expression

$$x(i) = x_0 + i \times h$$

The appropriate i for any given value of x can be found by subtracting x_0, dividing the remainder by the size of the intervals h, and truncating the result to an integer. That is, we can perform the following steps, using a real variable R and an integer variable I:

$$R \leftarrow (X - X0)/H$$
$$I \leftarrow R$$

Since we have defined $h = x(i + 1) - x(i)$, the formula given above for approximating y by linear interpolation reduces to

$$y = y(i) + [y(i + 1) - y(i)] \frac{x - x(i)}{h}$$

The first term, $y(i)$, can simply be read out of our table; the factor $\frac{x - x(i)}{h}$ needed to calculate the second term can be found easily by noting that

$$\frac{x - x(i)}{h} = \frac{x - x_0}{h} - \frac{x(i) - x_0}{h} = r - i$$

A complete function subprogram for calculating y by this method is shown in Program 6-1.

■ **Program 6.1   Linear interpolation**

```
LINEAR_INTERP: subprogram (Y,XO,H,N,X)
    Function subprogram to approximate a function by linear
    interpolation. The function value in array element Y(I)
    corresponds to the argument value

                   X(I) = XO + I*H

    If the value supplied for X is out of range, a warning message is
    printed and the value of the nearest endpoint is returned as the
    value of the function.
    integer I,N
    real Y(N),XO,H,X,Z,R,LINEAR_INTERP
        R ← (X − XO)/H
        I ← R
        if I < 1 or I ≥ N
          . then
                output 'X VALUE OUT OF RANGE'
                if I < 1
                    then Z ← Y(1)
                    else Z ← Y(N)
                    endif
            else
                R ← R − I
                Z ← Y(I) + (Y(I + 1) − Y(I))*R
            endif
        return (Z)
    endsubprogram LINEAR_INTERP
```

If the points are not equally spaced, an array of x values must be supplied along with those for y. The program must then search for a value of i such that $x(i) \leq x < x(i + 1)$. Since the x values are stored in order, this can be done with a fast binary search (see Chapter 1) if there are enough points to warrant it. In some applications, a particular function will be calculated for many neighboring values of x. In that case, we can use the previous value of i as a first guess for the value of i to be used in the next approximation. Such a program would operate by first checking to see whether the value of x is between $x(i)$ and $x(i + 1)$ for the last i used. If not, a sequential search forward or backward can be used to find the appropriate i.

Higher-order interpolation is usually used to achieve greater accuracy or greater smoothness. If we are interested only in the closeness of the approximation, we usually use more than two points to determine a polynomial function that passes through those points. For example, we can take three adjacent points, say the points on the curve corresponding to $x = x(i - 1)$, $x = x(i)$, and $x = x(i + 1)$, and find the coefficients of a quadratic polynomial $ax^2 + bx + c$ that passes through those points. Then, in the neighborhood of $x = x(i)$, we can approximate the function by that quadratic polynomial. If the accuracy is still insufficient, we can determine a cubic (third-order) polynomial by using four points.

This process can be continued: for each additional point we use, we increase the order of the polynomial by 1. If $n + 1$ points are used, an nth degree polynomial can be found that will go through those points, and its value can be calculated at any intermediate point. In practice, the polynomial is not directly calculated. Instead, schemes to generate the approximation using successively more points are employed. The process can be stopped when enough points have been used to get the desired accuracy. In principle, one could form the polynomial passing through all of the known values, but that is inefficient (because too many points are used) and could lead to large numerical errors.

At times we are also concerned with the smoothness of the approximation. Ship and automobile designers, for example, are interested in approximating smooth curves for the surfaces of hulls and fenders. In this case, higher-order polynomials are used to avoid the sharp bends at the joints of the *piecewise-linear* approximation in Figure 6-2. The curves given by these polynomials are similar to the "French curve" used in drafting to draw a smooth line connecting a number of points. Such curves, called *splines*, are very important in computer graphics and computer-aided design, but, unfortunately, are beyond the scope of this text.

PROBLEMS

1 Program a linear-interpolation function for unequally spaced points. The parameters should be arrays X and Y, each of dimension n, an x value XV (we are already using the name X for one of the arrays), and the integer N.

2 Suppose you are given two *n*-element arrays, X and Y, containing values of a function *y* corresponding to argument values *x*. Suppose further that the signs of Y(1) and Y(N) differ, and that the values X(I) are in increasing order as *i* increases. Write a program to find a value XO such that the corresponding value of the function is zero, assuming that the function can be approximated by linear interpolation between the tabulated values.

3 Suppose you are given a function tabulated at equal intervals—that is, the array element Y(I) gives the value of the function for $x = x_0 + h*i$, *i* from 1 to *n*. Write a subprogram to find all zeroes of the function, if any, between $x_0 + h$ and $x_0 + n*h$ by linear interpolation. (A *zero* of the function is a value of *x* for which the corresponding value of the function is zero.) Your subprogram should leave the number of zeroes found in an output parameter M and the values of the solution in an array ZERO(I), for *i* from 1 to *m*. (You will have to dimension ZERO by $n - 1$, as there may be that many solutions.)

7

Least-Squares Approximation

■　　　■　　　■　　　■　　　■　　　■

Least-squares approximation can be used to derive a simple function that approximates the observed results of an experiment. This application frequently arises when a scientist hypothesizes a formula governing a process and then wishes to measure the coefficients in that formula. Suppose, for example, that we wish to measure the acceleration due to gravity, g, by dropping an object and measuring its velocity after a given period of time. Since the velocity of an object starting from rest at time 0 is gt after t seconds, g can be found by measuring the velocity after 1 second. If this is found to be 980 centimeters per second, then we can conclude that g is 980 centimeters per second per second—or can we? Clearly there will be experimental error. Consequently, we may repeat our experiment a number of times and average the results, hoping thereby to reduce the experimental error. Before deciding the best way of averaging the results to reduce the amount of error, we need to consider the nature of the errors.

The first and most obvious cause of experimental error is *measurement error*. Because instruments can only be read with limited accuracy, typically between 0.1% and 1.0%, we can expect only two or three decimal digits of precision in the measurements. These errors are similar to rounding errors in computation: they are random and unpredictable, although we do have some idea of their worst-case size.

The second cause of error is consistent deviations in experimental conditions. For example, in the object-dropping experiment, the device that releases the object at time 0 may give it a small initial velocity u. In that case, the velocity after t seconds will be $u + gt$ instead of gt. This constant *bias*, u, will make g appear larger if u is positive or smaller if u is negative. Consequently, rather than just calculating g, we should also attempt to calculate u. That is, we hypothesize a formula $v = u + gt$ connecting our experimental observations of time t and velocity v, and calculate both g and u.

How can we do this? One way is to take two measurements, say v_1 after time t_1 and v_2 after time t_2, and solve for u and g in the equations

$$v_1 = u + gt_1$$
$$v_2 = u + gt_2$$

These are two equations in two unknowns and so, if t_1 and t_2 are different, can be solved uniquely. Unfortunately, we still have the problem of measurement errors, so we would like to take many measurements at different times and use the information to make a "best" estimate of the values of u and g.

Figure 7-1 shows a graph of $v = u + gt$ for particular values of u and g, along with a set of measurements that might be taken in an experiment.

FIGURE 7-1   Measurements and hypothesized function

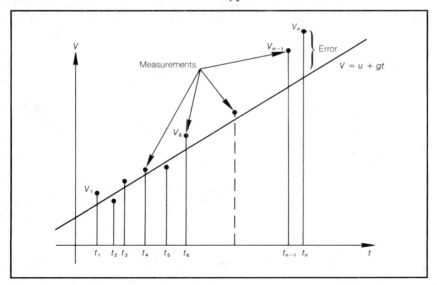

Some of the measurements are very close to the assumed function, so we can find no reason to disbelieve the graph on the basis of these measurements. However, some of the measurements, such as v_{n-1} and v_n, are a long way from the line representing the function, leading us to suspect that u and g should be changed so that the function is closer to those measurements. What we wish to do is choose u and g so that the function is not too far away from any of the measured points, since we are prepared to accept small deviations but disbelieve large ones. Consequently, in trying to estimate how far the measurements are from the function, we want to give more weight to points farther away. If we take the sum of the squares of the errors, that is,

$$D = (v_1 - u - gt_1)^2 + (v_2 - u - gt_2)^2 + \cdots + (v_n - u - gt_n)^2$$

we get a number D that is never negative, and becomes larger if any measured point is moved farther away from the graph of the function. Furthermore, the contribution to D is much larger for points that are farther away than for points that are close. For example, if a point is twice as far from the graph of the function as another point, it contributes four times as much to D, because of the effect of the square. Hence it seems very reasonable to pick u and g so as to make D as small as possible. This process is called finding a *least-squares fit*—in this case, a *linear least-squares fit*, because the approximating function, $u + gt$, is linear in the variable t. (The use of a least-squares fit as the most reasonable approximation can be justified on other, more technical grounds as well.)

The least-squares fit has one very useful feature: it is easy to calculate the coefficients that make D as small as possible. The derivation we will give uses simple calculus; the same result can be derived without calculus, but it takes considerably longer. Readers who do not know calculus can skip the derivation and go directly to the result in equations (7.1) and (7.2).

The sum of the square errors is

$$D = \sum_{i=1}^{n} (v_i - u - gt_i)^2$$

The values of u and g that minimize this expression are found by differentiating D with respect to u and g separately and equating the derivatives to zero. Thus we get

$$\frac{\partial D}{\partial u} = 0 = -2 \sum_{i=1}^{n} (v_i - u - gt_i)$$

and

$$\frac{\partial D}{\partial g} = 0 = -2 \sum_{i=1}^{n} (v_i - u - gt_i)t_i$$

These equations can be rewritten as

$$u \sum_{i=1}^{n} 1 + g \sum_{i=1}^{n} t_i = \sum_{i=1}^{n} v_i$$

and

$$u \sum_{i=1}^{n} t_i + g \sum_{i=1}^{n} t_i^2 = \sum_{i=1}^{n} v_i t_i$$

If we write

$$T_0 = \sum_{i=1}^{n} 1 = n; \qquad T_1 = \sum_{i=1}^{n} t_i; \qquad T_2 = \sum_{i=1}^{n} T_i^2$$

$$V_0 = \sum_{i=1}^{n} v_i; \qquad V_1 = \sum_{i=1}^{n} v_i t_i$$

(7.1)

the equations determining u and g are

$$uT_0 + gT_1 = V_0$$
$$uT_1 + gT_2 = V_1$$

(7.2)

which can be solved for u and g. As long as not all the values of t_i are identical, it can be shown that there is a unique solution for u and g.

Least-squares fitting is not restricted to linear approximations. For example, we could have chosen to measure g by finding out how far an object fell in t seconds, with $t \neq 1$. The formula for the distance fallen, d, is

$$d = s + ut + gt^2/2$$

where s is the initial distance, u the initial velocity, and g the acceleration due to gravity. If a series of measurements, t_i and d_i, are taken, we can choose s, u, and g so as to minimize

$$D = \sum_{i=1}^{n} (d_i - s - ut_i - gt_i^2/2)^2$$

If we do this, we obtain

$$sT_0 + uT_1 + \frac{g}{2}T_2 = D_0$$

$$sT_1 + uT_2 + \frac{g}{2}T_3 = D_1$$

$$sT_2 + uT_3 + \frac{g}{2}T_4 = D_2$$

where

$$T_0 = \sum_{i=1}^{n} 1 = n; \qquad T_1 = \sum_{i=1}^{n} t_i; \qquad T_2 = \sum_{i=1}^{n} t_i^2; \qquad \ldots ;$$

$$D_0 = \sum_{i=1}^{n} d_i; \qquad D_1 = \sum_{i=1}^{n} d_i t_i; \qquad D_2 = \sum_{i=1}^{n} d_i t_i^2$$

These three equations can be solved for s, u, and g.

Example 7.1
Linear Least-Squares Fit

Suppose we expect a measurement of the temperature, y, of a body to vary with time, t, according to the equation $y = a + be^{-t}$. We have the following measurements at various times t_i:

i	t_i	y_i
1	0	1.26
2	1	1.10
3	2	0.895
4	4	0.758
5	8	0.761

We wish to find the coefficients a and b.

It seems that this is not a straight-line approximation, so our linear least-squares method is of no value. However, we can change to a new variable, $x = e^{-t}$, so that $y = a + bx$. This formula is linear and we can do a least-squares fit, so we proceed to form

$$X_p = \sum_{i=1}^{5} x_i^p$$

$$Y_p = \sum_{i=1}^{5} y_i x_i^p$$

The results are shown in Table 7-1.

We substitute these values in

$$X_0 a + X_1 b = Y_0$$
$$X_1 a + X_2 b = Y_1$$

TABLE 7-1 Values of x_i, y_i, x_i^2, and $y_i x_i$

i	t_i	$x_i = e^{-t_i}$	y_i	x_i^2	$y_i x_i$
1	0	1.00000	1.26	1.00000	1.26000
2	1	0.36788	1.10	0.13534	0.40467
3	2	0.13534	0.895	0.01832	0.12113
4	4	0.01832	0.758	0.00033	0.01389
5	8	0.00033	0.761	0.00000	0.00025
Sum		1.52187	4.774	1.15399	1.79994
		X_1	Y_0	X_2	Y_1

to get

$$5a + 1.52187b = 4.774$$
$$1.52187a + 1.15399b = 1.79994$$

These equations have the solution

$$a = 0.80197$$
$$b = 0.50213$$

so the least-squares fit for this data is

$$y = 0.80197 + 0.50213e^{-t}$$

Least-squares fitting can also be used to approximate functions. In Chapter 6 we used linear interpolation to approximate a function measured experimentally. Alternatively, we can approximate a function by a polynomial and determine the coefficients of the polynomial by the least-squares method. Numerical approximations to the function can then be obtained by evaluating the polynomial.

Although the simple techniques we have examined above are adequate for least-squares fitting, they are numerically poor for fitting higher-order approximations such as high-degree polynomials. For these problems, methods based on *orthogonal polynomials* should be used. The discussion of these methods is beyond the scope of this text, but the underlying principle is the same as that for the simple approach discussed above. Fortunately, there are a number of good library programs in most computer centers that will permit the user to solve least-squares problems accurately and efficiently.

PROBLEMS

1 Suppose the following measurements are taken in an experiment:

x	1	2	3	4
y	4	1	0	-1

Find M and B in $y = Mx + B$ by a least-squares technique.

2 Suppose we take a series of readings of the torque, T, and the height, h, of end B of the rod AB of length r which is pivoting about A, as shown in the diagram.

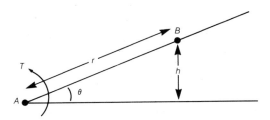

The rod pivots through an angle θ due to the torque, and the relation between the angle and the torque is

$$T = K + L\theta$$

where K and L are unknown constants. The angle θ is related to the measurement h by

$$h = r \sin \theta$$

If the readings taken are

T	0	1	3	4	6
h	0.01	0.12	0.32	0.39	0.59

compute K and L by the linear least-squares technique, given $r = 1.2$.

8

Minimax Approximations

■   ■   ■   ■   ■   ■

In the previous chapter we looked at the problem of approximating a function whose form was known but whose measurements were tainted by errors. Because we wanted to attach more importance to measurements that were significantly different from the hypothesized function, we squared the error and minimized the sum of the squares. In some situations we do not want to give so much weight to values far from the average, so we might choose some other combination of the errors to minimize. For example, we might just sum the absolute values of the errors and choose the coefficients that minimize that sum. This leads to what is called the best L_1 approximation. (The least-squares approximation is called the best L_2 approximation.) There are many other approximations of this sort. A particularly important one is the minimax approximation, in which we ask that the coefficients be chosen so that the largest of the errors is as small as possible. (The name means that over all approximations, we choose the one that *mini*mizes the *max*imum error.) This is also called the best L_∞ approximation.

Minimax approximation is also an important tool in the approximation of known, expensive-to-compute functions by simpler functions that are less expensive to compute. In this case it is clear why a minimax approximation is the most appropriate form of approximation: we would like to write code that, over its range of application, will introduce the smallest error of any code we might write that would take the same amount of time to execute. We will examine minimax techniques for this type of problem.

Suppose we are asked to write a subprogram that will approximate $\sin(x)$ to limited precision for small values of x and will operate very rapidly (presumably because it is to be used frequently in a calculation). We can start with the power series for the sine and discard all but a few terms. Suppose we discard all but the first term. We then have the approximation

$$\sin(x) = x$$

If the maximum error that can be tolerated is e, the largest value of x for which this approximation is sufficiently accurate is the value x_0 for which $x_0 = \sin(x_0) + e$, as shown in Figure 8-1. However, if we choose another linear approximation, say

$$\sin(x) = ax$$

where a is less than 1, we may be able to extend the range of x for which the approximation is within e to all x less than some larger x_1, again as shown in Figure 8-1. The desired property of the straight line $y = ax$ in

FIGURE 8-1   Linear approximations to $\sin(x)$

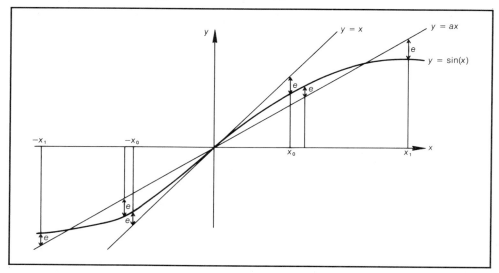

FIGURE 8-2   Chebyshev approximation to sin(x)

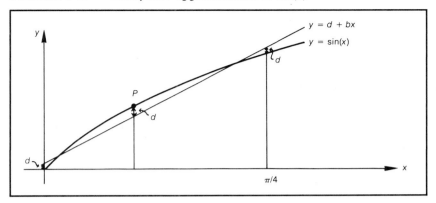

relation to the function sin(x) over the interval $(-x_1, x_1)$ is that, of all linear functions, its maximum deviation from sin(x) is the smallest. That is, if we take any other linear function and calculate the largest value of [linear function $-$ sin(x)] over the interval $(-x_1, x_1)$, we will get a number larger than e. For this reason, we call this the *minimax* or *Chebyshev* approximation to sin(x) over this interval.

Chebyshev approximations, named for the Russian mathematician Pafnuti Lvovich Chebyshev, are used in many computer routines. They are not limited to linear polynomials: the polynomial of a certain fixed degree is found whose maximum deviation from the sine over the interval in question is minimum.

Linear Chebyshev approximations are not too difficult to calculate for many problems. For example, if we wish to approximate sin(x) over the interval $(0, \pi/4)$ with a linear function, we will choose the function shown in Figure 8-2. The error at $x = 0$ is some number d, the error at the extreme on the other side (P in the figure) is $-d$, and the error at $\pi/4$ is d again. That is, the worst-case error occurs at three points, and the sign of the error at those points alternates. It can be shown that the Chebyshev approximation always has this property for linear approximations. Generally, the Chebyshev approximation by an nth degree polynomial has $n + 2$ extreme errors with alternating signs.

When we approximate a function, $f(x)$, whose values are known only at a discrete set of points, (x_i, y_i), where $y_i = f(x_i)$, we choose the approximation that minimizes the maximum deviation at those points. Thus, if the minimax approximation is $p(x)$, $p(x)$ is chosen so that

$$\max_i |y_i - f(x_i)|$$

is minimum.

PROBLEMS

1 Find the minimax approximation to $\cos(w)$ over the interval $0°$ to $180°$, using a linear function.

2 The following values have been taken for a function $f(x)$:

x	0	1	5	6
$f(x)$	1	1	2	2

What is the minimax linear approximation to $f(x)$? What about the minimax quadratic approximation? (In other words, an approximation of the form $a_0 + a_1 x + a_2 x^2$?)

P A R T

III

SOLUTION OF EQUATIONS AND NUMERICAL ERRORS

■   ■   ■   ■

Many scientific and engineering applications require the solution of *nonlinear equations* that cannot be solved directly by arithmetic operations. Examples include second- and higher-order polynomials, such as

$$x^3 - x + 4.7 = 0$$
$$x^4 + 2x^2 - x + 4 = 0$$

and equations involving nonlinear functions, such as

$$\sin(x) - 0.5x + 1.3 = 0$$

Such an equation may have one real solution, none, or many. These three cases are illustrated in Figures III-1 to III-3, which show the graphs of the left-hand sides of the three equations above. Solutions of these equations occur where the graphs cross the x-axis. In more complicated situations, the problem solver may be faced with several equations to be solved simultaneously; for example, the equations

$$x^2 + y^2 - 2x - 2y - 7 = 0$$
$$x^2 + y^2 + 2x + 2y - 7 = 0$$

FIGURE III-1   One real solution

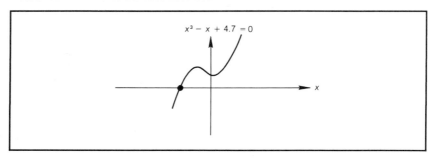

$$x^3 - x + 4.7 = 0$$

FIGURE III-2   No real solution

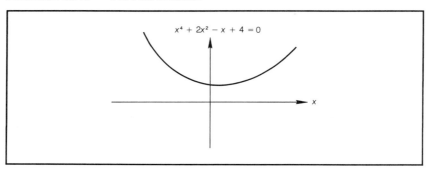

$$x^4 + 2x^2 - x + 4 = 0$$

FIGURE III-3   Many real solutions

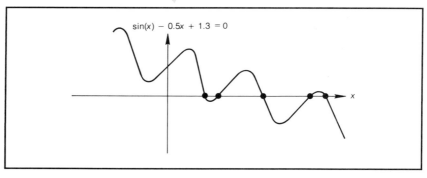

$$\sin(x) - 0.5x + 1.3 = 0$$

(these are two intersecting circles). In some cases, solutions can be found by analytical methods, but in many cases we use a computer to find approximate solutions. Even if the solutions can, in principle, be found analytically, in many cases use of a computer is necessary because of the time involved.

Many important classes of problems are *linear*—that is, each unknown is multiplied only by a constant. We can find methods of computing the solutions for these problems to as much accuracy as desired, and we will study their solution in the first chapter of this part. If, however, the equations are nonlinear, we can normally do no better than to approximate the solution. Usually this is done by making a linear approximation to the equation, and then using methods for linear equations to solve the simplified problem. In Chapter 10 we will look at the problem of solving a single nonlinear equation in one unknown. Chapter 11 examines several equations in several unknowns, and the last chapter of this section looks at the problems of numerical errors, both those that can arise in the solution of equations and those that arise in other numerical computations.

9

Solution of
Linear Equations

■   ■   ■   ■   ■   ■   ■

We all know how to solve a pair of simultaneous equations in two unknowns, such as

$$3x + 6y = 15$$
$$2x + 3y = 8$$

Although we don't usually think about the details of the steps we take, our
approach to such problems is based on the fact that we cannot directly
solve such a problem, and so must first reduce it to a simpler one that we
can solve directly. In this case, we reduce the problem to one equation in
one unknown. To do so, we divide the first equation by 3 (the coefficient
of x) to get

$$x + 2y = 5$$

which expresses the value of x in terms of the value of y. Then we substitute this value of x into the second equation to get an equation for y

only. One way of doing the second step is to multiply the equation obtained from the first step by the coefficient of x in the second equation (in this case 2) to get

$$2x + 4y = 10$$

and subtract this from the second equation, getting

$$-y = -2$$

or $y = 2$. We can now substitute this value back into the equation for x to find that $x = 1$. These steps are tabulated below.

Initial equations	$\begin{cases} 3x + 6y = 15 \\ 2x + 3y = 8 \end{cases}$	(a) (b)
Divide eq. (a) by 3 Eq. (c) now replaces eq. (a)	$x + 2y = 5$	(c)
Multiply eq. (c) by 2	$2x + 4y = 10$	(d)
Subtract eq. (d) from eq. (b)	$-y = -2$	(e)
Divide eq. (e) by -1 Eq. (f) replaces eq. (b)	$y = 2$	(f)
Multiply eq. (f) by 2	$2y = 4$	(g)
Subtract eq. (g) from eq. (c)	$x = 1$	(h)

The solution can be found in equations (f) and (h), which have actually replaced the first two.

Large systems of linear equations frequently arise in scientific, engineering, and business applications. For example, problems in *operations research*, which arise in management decisions concerning the best ways to produce and distribute products, may involve tens of thousands of equations in as many unknowns. We need a digital computer to solve them, but even with a computer we need a method. As with a simple pair of equations, we try to reduce the problem to a simpler one.

Suppose we are given the n equations

$$\begin{aligned}
a_{11}x_1 + a_{12}x_2 + \cdots + a_{1n}x_n &= b_1 \\
a_{21}x_1 + a_{22}x_2 + \cdots + a_{2n}x_n &= b_2 \\
&\vdots \\
a_{n1}x_1 + a_{n2}x_2 + \cdots + a_{nn}x_n &= b_n
\end{aligned}$$

$$(9.1)$$

in the n unknowns $x_1, x_2, \ldots, x_n$, where $a_{11}, a_{12}, \ldots, a_{nn}$ and $b_1, b_2, \ldots, b_n$ are coefficients. We want to find values of $x_1, \ldots x_n$ that satisfy these equations. If we could use the first equation to eliminate x_1 from each of the remaining $n - 1$ equations, we would have a system of $n - 1$ equations in $n - 1$ unknowns—a smaller problem that we could try to solve by the same approach, until eventually we would reduce the problem to one equation in one unknown, which we could solve directly. This can be done by the following steps: Divide the first equation by a_{11} to get

$$x_1 + \frac{a_{12}}{a_{11}} x_2 + \cdots + \frac{a_{1n}}{a_{11}} x_n = \frac{b_1}{a_{11}} \tag{9.2}$$

This is another linear equation equivalent to the original one, but with the coefficient of x_1 changed to 1. Next we subtract a_{21} times (9.2) from the second of equations (9.1) to get rid of x_1. We get

$$0 \cdot x_1 + \left(a_{22} - a_{21} \frac{a_{12}}{a_{11}} \right) x_2 + \cdots + \left(a_{2n} - a_{21} \frac{a_{1n}}{a_{11}} \right) x_n$$

$$= \left(b_2 - a_{21} \frac{b_1}{a_{11}} \right) \tag{9.3}$$

This is another linear equation satisfied by any point $x_1, \ldots, x_n$ that satisfies the first two of equations (9.1). Note that when we wrote the original equations, (9.1), and when we write the modified equations, (9.2) and (9.3), we always write the form "coefficient times x_1 plus coefficient times x_2 plus . . . plus coefficient times x_n equals number." The names of the unknowns $x_1, \ldots, x_n$, plus signs, and the equal sign always appear, so there is no need to write them down. We need only write the coefficients a_{ij} and the numbers b_i. We just have to remember that the other symbols are assumed to be there. Thus we can start with the rectangular array

$$
\begin{matrix}
a_{11} & a_{12} & \cdots & a_{1n} & b_1 \\
a_{21} & a_{22} & \cdots & a_{2n} & b_2 \\
\cdot & & & & \\
\cdot & & & & \\
\cdot & & & & \\
a_{n1} & a_{n2} & \cdots & a_{nn} & b_n
\end{matrix}
$$

The first step is to divide the first row (that is, the first equation) by a_{11}. We call a_{11} the *pivot element*. This changes the first row so that the new element in the (1, 1) position is 1. We will call the element in the (i, j) position a_{ij} regardless of how many times it has been changed, because we are going to store the coefficients in an array A(I, J) when we solve this problem by computer. Hence the result of dividing the first row by the pivot element is

$$\begin{array}{ccccc} 1 & a_{12} & \cdots & a_{1n} & b_1 \\ a_{21} & a_{22} & \cdots & a_{2n} & b_2 \\ \cdot & & & & \\ \cdot & & & & \\ \cdot & & & & \\ a_{n1} & a_{n2} & \cdots & a_{nn} & b_n \end{array}$$

The next step is to subtract a_{21} times the first row (equation) from the second row (equation) to reduce the first element of the second row to zero. This process is continued by subtracting a_{31} times the first row from the third row, and so on, until all elements below the pivot element in the first column are zero. The array now has the form

$$\begin{array}{ccccc} 1 & a_{12} & \cdots & a_{1n} & b_1 \\ 0 & a_{22} & \cdots & a_{2n} & b_2 \\ \cdot & & & & \\ \cdot & & & & \\ \cdot & & & & \\ 0 & a_{n2} & \cdots & a_{nn} & b_n \end{array}$$

If we could find the solution for $x_2, x_3, \ldots, x_n$, the first row could be solved for x_1. The last $n - 1$ rows now represent $n - 1$ equations in the $n - 1$ unknowns $x_2, \ldots, x_n$. The same process can be applied to these, using a_{22} as the next pivot. The second row is divided by a_{22}, giving an array of the form

$$\begin{array}{cccccc} 1 & a_{12} & a_{13} & \cdots & a_{1n} & b_1 \\ 0 & 1 & a_{23} & \cdots & a_{2n} & b_2 \\ 0 & a_{32} & a_{33} & \cdots & a_{3n} & b_3 \\ \cdot & & & & & \\ \cdot & & & & & \\ \cdot & & & & & \\ 0 & a_{n2} & a_{n3} & \cdots & a_{nn} & b_n \end{array}$$

Now a_{32} times the second row is subtracted from the third row to put a zero in the (3, 2) position. This is repeated with $a_{42}, \ldots, a_{n2}$ to put zeros in every element below the pivot a_{22} in the second column. The array now has the form

$$\begin{array}{cccccc} 1 & a_{12} & a_{13} & \cdots & a_{1n} & b_1 \\ 0 & 1 & a_{23} & \cdots & a_{2n} & b_2 \\ 0 & 0 & a_{33} & \cdots & a_{3n} & b_3 \\ \cdot & & & & & \\ \cdot & & & & & \\ \cdot & & & & & \\ 0 & 0 & a_{n3} & \cdots & a_{nn} & b_n \end{array}$$

Now the last $n - 2$ rows represent $n - 2$ equations in the $n - 2$ unknowns $x_3, \ldots, x_n$. Again we can repeat the process by making a_{33}, the new pivot, equal to one and $a_{k3} = 0$ for $k = 4, 5, \ldots, n$. The process continues until all pivots a_{kk} are 1 and all elements below the pivots are zero. Notice that the pivots are the diagonal elements of the part of the array containing the a_{ij}, and that all elements below the diagonal are zero. We say that the resulting array is *triangular*, because only a triangular part of it is nonzero, as shown in Figure 9-1.

The process we have been describing is called *Gaussian elimination*, after the mathematician Karl Friedrich Gauss. In the triangular form, the last row represents the equation $x_n = b_n$. Thus we have the solution for x_n. With this we can eliminate x_n from each of the other equations by subtracting a_{kn} times the last equation from the kth equation for $k = 1, 2, \ldots, n - 1$. The result is shown in Figure 9-2. Now the next to the last

FIGURE 9-1   Triangular array

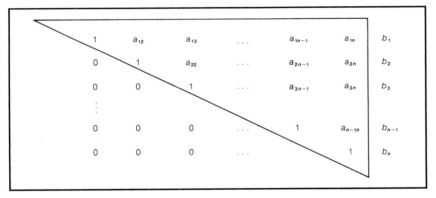

FIGURE 9-2   Array after back-substitution

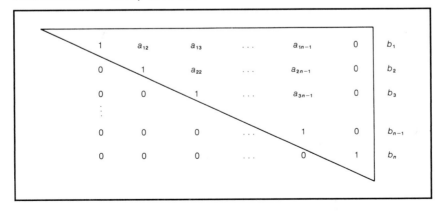

row tells us that $x_{n-1} = b_{n-1}$. Next we can subtract suitable multiples of that row from the earlier rows to put zeros above the diagonal in the next to the last column. This step can be repeated, working back up the matrix until all the elements above the diagonal are zero. Now we have a *diagonal* array, and the *i*th equation reads $x_i = b_i$. Thus the solution to the problem is found in the vector B. This second stage of the process is called *back-substitution*.

The implementation of this method in Program 9-1 uses a single array A of *n* by *n* + 1 elements to store the coefficients a_{ij} and b_i. The elements a_{ij} are stored in A(I, J) in the usual way. The elements b_i are stored in A(I, N + 1), the last column of the array. This is convenient because a

■ **Program 9.1   Outline of program to solve linear equations**

```
GAUSS: subprogram (A,N)
    Solve the system of N linear equations specified by the coefficients
    in the N-by-(N + 1) array A. The Ith equation is

    A(I, 1)*X1 + A(I, 2)*X2 + ··· + A(I, N)*XN = A(I,N + 1)

    On completion, the solution X1, X2, . . ., XN is in the last
    column of A, elements A(1, N + 1), A(2, N + 1), . . .,
    A(N, N + 1). The elements of A are changed by the subprogram.
    real A(N, N + 1),P,E
    integer I,J,K,N
        convert A to triangular form
        back-substitute
        return
    endsubprogram GAUSS
```

■ **Program 9.1a   Code segment to convert A to triangular form**

```
convert A to triangular form: codesegment
    The array A is modified by row operations consisting of division of
    all elements of one row by a common value, and subtraction of a
    multiple of one row from another.
        do for I ← 1 to N
            divide row I by A(I,I)
            do for J ← I + 1 to N
                subtract a multiple of row I from row J
                so that A(J,I) = 0
            enddo
        enddo
    endcodesegment
```

■ Program 9.1b   Code segment to divide row by pivot element

```
divide row I by A(I,I): codesegment
   do for J ← I + 1 to N + 1
      A(I,J) ← A(I,J)/A(I,I)
      enddo
   endcodesegment
```

■ Program 9.1c   Code segment to eliminate element A(J,I)

```
subtract a multiple of row I from row J . . . :
codesegment
   do for K ← I + 1 to N + 1
      A(J,K) ← A(J,K) − A(I,K)*A(J,I)
      enddo
   endcodesegment
```

■ Program 9.1d   Code segment to do back-substitution

```
back-substitute: codesegment
   Outer loop to compute each xⱼ
   outer: do for J ← N − 1 to 1 by −1
      E ← 0.0
      Inner loop to form sum of known aⱼₖxₖ
      inner: do for K ← J + 1 to N
         E ← E + A(K,N + 1)*A(J,K)
         enddo inner
      A(J,N + 1) ← A(J,N + 1) − E
      enddo outer
   endcodesegment
```

study of the algorithm reveals that the operations on the element b_i are identical to the operations on every element of the ith row of a_{ij}. Program 9-1 is presented at successively more detailed levels of refinement. The outline consists of two main segments: conversion of A to triangular form, which is given in successive levels of refinement in Programs 9-1a through 9-1c, and back-substitution, which is given in Program 9-1d. We have used the keywords **codesegment** and **endcodesegment** in Programs 9-1a through 9-1d because we intend these segments to be substituted back into the original outline. (They could be defined as subprograms and called in the outline, but the final program will not be long enough to warrant the extra computer time taken by procedure calls.)

Program 9-1a gives the code segment to triangularize the array in outline form. This segment is refined further in the next two programs. The division of row I by $A(I, I)$ is shown in Program 9-1b. This code does not bother to divide elements to the left of the diagonal element $A(I, I)$, because they are known to be zero. Neither does it bother to divide the diagonal element itself, because the answer is known to be one. There is no need to assign values to variables known to be zero or one, because they are not used again in the computation.

Program 9-1c gives the code to subtract $A(J, I)$ times row I from row J. Since the first $I - 1$ elements in both rows are known to be zero, there is again no need to perform arithmetic on them. Since the result for $A(J, I)$ is known to be zero, there is no point in computing or storing it either.

It is numerically preferable to change the order of operations slightly in the back-substitution segment (Program 9-1d). After the triangularization, we know that the value of x_n is in $A(N, N + 1)$. Hence we can write

$$x_{n-1} = b_{n-1} - x_n * a_{n-1,n}$$

which can be implemented by

```
A(N - 1, N + 1)←A(N - 1, N + 1)
    - A(N, N + 1)*A(N - 1, N)
```

leaving the result in $A(N - 1, N + 1)$. After we have calculated the values $x_n, x_{n-1}, \ldots, x_{j+1}$ in the elements $A(K, N + 1)$, for K from N to $J + 1$, we can calculate x_j by

$$x_j = -(x_{j+1} * a_{j,j+1} + x_{j+2} * a_{j,j+2} + \cdots + x_n * a_{j,n}) + b_j$$

In Program 9-1d, the term in parentheses is accumulated in the variable E.

Before we bring the pieces of this program together into a unit, there are two factors that should be considered: speed and accuracy. In Program 9-1b each element in a row is divided by the element $A(I, I)$. Execution of the statement in the third line of that segment requires that the address of the cell containing $A(I, I)$ be calculated by the computer in order to read the value of the divisor from memory. Since I does not change inside the loop, it is not necessary to calculate the address of $A(I, I)$ on every pass through the loop. Indeed, many compilers will recognize this fact and produce object code that is "optimized." However, if the compiler does not do this optimization, the programmer can do it by rewriting the loop as

```
P←A(I, I)
do for J←I + 1 to N + 1
   A(I, J)←A(I, J)/P
   enddo
```

Similarly, in Program 9-1c, the element A(J, I) does not change inside the loop, so the loop can be rewritten as

```
E←A(J, I)
do for K←1 + 1 to N + 1
   A(J, K)←A(J, K) − A(I, K)*E
   enddo
```

Numerical accuracy in this type of process will not be considered until the next chapter. However, there is one situation in which the code shown clearly will not work: if the value of A(I, I) is zero for some I in Program 9-1b, the program will fail on a "divide by zero" error. Suppose that A(I, I) is zero when the time comes for this division. Notice that at this stage of the process, the rows $I, I + 1, I + 2, \ldots, N$ are similar, in that each has zeros in columns $1, 2, \ldots, I - 1$. Clearly, the solution of a system of linear equations is not affected by the order in which we write them, so let us simply switch two of the equations, say rows I and K. If A(K, I) is nonzero before the switch, A(I, I) will be nonzero after the switch. Therefore, before dividing row I by A(I, I), we will make sure that A(I, I) is nonzero by switching rows if necessary. This will be possible if any one of the elements A(K, I), for K from I to N, is nonzero. (If all are zero, the problem does not have a well-defined solution.) It is convenient for reasons of accuracy (see Chapter 12) to switch rows so that the largest of the A(K, I) elements appears in position A(I, I). Program 9-1e is a modification of 9-1b that incorporates this change.

■ **Program 9.1e   Improved version of Program 9.1b**

```
divide row I by A(I,I): codesegment
   Find largest A(K,I)
   K ← I
   P ← ABS(A(I,I))
   do for J ← I + 1 to N
      if ABS(A(J,I)) > P
         then
            K ← J
            P ← ABS(A(J,I))
         endif
      enddo
```

```
if P = 0.0
   | then
   |     output 'NO WELL DEFINED SOLUTION,
   |     CALCULATION TERMINATED'
   |     return
   | endif
If K ≠ I, switch rows I and K.
if K ≠ I
   | then
   |     do for J ← I to N + 1
   |        | P ← A(I,J)
   |        | A(I,J) ← A(K,J)
   |        | A(K,J) ← P
   |        | enddo
   | endif
Now divide by the pivot element
P ← A(I,I)
do for J ← I + 1 to N + 1
   | A(I,J) ← A(I,J)/P
   | enddo
endcodesegment
```

PROBLEMS

1 Some systems of linear equations, called *sparse* equations, have large numbers of zero coefficients. If there are many zeros, special techniques can be used to reduce the amount of storage and arithmetic performed in the solution of the system. If there are not many zeros, these techniques are not valuable, but some speed improvement can be obtained by testing to see whether some of the elements below the diagonal are already 'zero and omitting the elimination step for the corresponding rows. Modify Program 9-1c to include such a test.

2 Compute the number of times that each statement in Programs 9-1c to 9-1e is executed for $N = 3$, 4, and 5. (Assume that the conditions in the **if** statements are always true except that $P ≠ 0.0$.) Can you give the number of times each statement is executed as a function of N? You will need the relations

$$1 + 2 + 3 + \cdots + N = N(N + 1)/2$$
$$1^2 + 2^2 + 3^2 + \cdots + N^2 = N(N + 1)(2N + 1)/6$$

3 Program 9-1 can fail to find a solution because of overflow. The most likely place for this to occur is in the step where each element in a row is divided by the pivot element in Program 9-1b. An alternative scheme is to leave this step for later. In that case, the elimination step must be changed by replacing $A(J,I)$ in 9-1c with $E = A(J,I)/A(I,I)$.

(This cannot cause overflow—why?) Also, the back-substitution step must be changed to divide the value computed for x_j by $A(J, J)$. This can cause an overflow, but a test can be programmed so that a return with $GAUSS = 0$ can be made if an overflow would occur. Modify the program in this way.

4 Program 9-1e swaps rows of the array A to put the largest element on the diagonal as a pivot. This process is time consuming. An alternative scheme is to use a one-dimensional array of pointers to indicate which row of A is used for the Ith pivot. Suppose this array is called ROW. Initially, ROW can be set so that $ROW(I)$ contains I for I from 1 to N. If, when selecting the pivot in the Ith column, the Kth row is selected, the Ith and Kth elements of ROW can be exchanged. Instead of swapping the Ith and Kth rows, we can reference the Ith row by $A(ROW(I), K)$ for K from 1 to N. If all references to rows of A are made through the array ROW in this way, Programs 9-1c to 9-1e will compute the solutions so that x_i is in $A(ROW(I), N + 1)$.
  a. Modify the programs in the manner described.
  b. Design a scheme to unscramble the answers, so that the solution for x_i is in $A(I, N + 1)$. (Hint: Scan through ROW, and if $ROW(I)$ is not I, move $A(ROW(I), N + 1)$ to $A(I, N + 1)$, saving the old value of $A(I, N + 1)$. Before continuing the scan, check $ROW(ROW(I))$ and find out what should be stored in $A(ROW(I), N + 1)$. Continue in this way until you get back to the Ith element, then continue the scan.)

5 Programs 9-1b to 9-1d do not set the values below the diagonal to zero, nor the values on the diagonal to one. In fact, the values that remain in the array $A(I, J)$ at the end of execution are precisely those that were used to divide the rows by and to multiply rows by before subtracting them from other rows in the elimination step. If we were given another set of *right-hand side* values, b_i, we could use the values left in the array $A(I, J)$ to perform the operations on the b_i that would have been done had those b_i values been provided initially, without doing any more operations on the values in the $A(I, J)$ array for $1 \leq J \leq N$. Use this idea to rewrite programs 9-1b to 9-1d so that they operate only on the *square* matrix $A(I, J)$, $1 \leq I, J \leq N$, and then write code that will take the values left in the $A(I, J)$ array and operate on a vector $B(I)$, $1 \leq I \leq N$, to produce a solution in B.

6 If the method used in Program 9-1e is used to avoid numerical problems, it is necessary to use the technique suggested in Problem 4 to remember which elements were used as pivots. Modify your answer to Problem 5 to do this.

10

Solving a
Nonlinear Equation

■　　　　■　　　　■　　　　■　　　　■　　　　■

We will discuss several methods that can be applied to the problem of finding solutions to $f(x) = 0$, where $f(x)$ is some nonlinear function of x. We call such solutions *zeros* of $f(x)$. Most methods of solution require only that we be able to evaluate $f(x)$ for any value of the argument x. We can immediately see one source of error in the answer: rounding error in evaluating $f(x)$. Since we cannot evaluate f exactly, the "graph" of $f(x)$ is effectively a "thick line." If we try to evaluate f with the unknown rounding errors, we may get any point inside this thick line. We want to know where the x-axis crosses the graph, but we can only find the *region* in which the x-axis lies within the thick line, as shown in Figure 10-1. It is evident that the smaller the slope of the graph near the origin, the larger the region of intersection and hence the larger the possible error. Whatever method of solution we use, we cannot hope to get more accuracy than that represented by this region of intersection.

The method itself can introduce additional errors. For example, the method of bisection discussed in Chapter 1 can be used if $f(x)$ is continuous and we are given two values of x for which $f(x)$ has opposite signs. This guarantees that we start with an interval that contains at least one

FIGURE 10-1   Effect of errors in evaluating $f(x)$

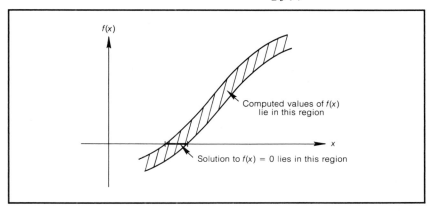

FIGURE 10-2   Error due to method

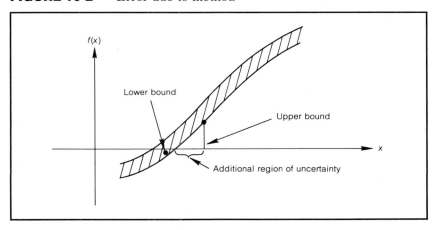

root. By making this interval successively smaller by factors of 2, we can reduce it to any desired size within the precision of the arithmetic used. The length of this interval can cause an additional error, as shown in Figure 10-2.

All the methods we will discuss for the solution of nonlinear equations are iterative methods, like the method of bisection. In any iterative method, we have to decide when to stop the iteration. The method of bisection has the desirable property that it gives upper and lower bounds on the solution, so that we have a bound on the error introduced by the method (that is, the truncation error). We must realize that we cannot make this bound arbitrarily small, because of the finite precision of the computer: we cannot reduce the interval between the upper and lower bounds below the minimum interval representable in the machine. Suppose we have a point L such that $f(L) < 0$ and a point U such that $f(U) > 0$, and suppose that U is the next larger number than L in the machine representation. The method of bisection calculates the midpoint of L and U as $(U + L)/2$. However, to machine precision, the value of this expression is either the point L or the point U. Therefore the next iteration of the method will give the same interval L to U as before, so there is no reason to continue. This is the closest we can get by any method of solution, although usually we will want to stop the iteration earlier. *In most problems of this sort, the rounding error in the machine (that is, the size of the smallest interval representable) is much less than the desired precision of the solution.*

10.1   REGULA FALSI METHOD

In the method of bisection, we evaluate the function but use only information about the sign. Suppose we try to use the size of the function as well. If the graph of the function is fairly straight, we can draw a straight line between the lower and upper points, and use this line to guess the point P where the function crosses the x-axis. (See Figure 10-3.) The point P is, we hope, a better approximation to the zero of the function than is the midpoint of the interval. As in the method of bisection, we form a new, smaller interval containing the solution. To do this we evaluate the function at the new point and decide, on the basis of the sign, which endpoint to replace with the new point P. In Figure 10-3, we see that the point P replaces the lower endpoint, because the sign of the function is negative at both points. This means that there is known to be a solution between P and the upper endpoint. This technique is called the *regula falsi method*, or *method of false position*.

The regula falsi method is guaranteed to give a solution, because we start with an interval known to contain a solution and always maintain such an interval. However, it may not give us upper and lower bounds that are close, as is demonstrated in Figure 10-3. In that example, the point P always replaces the lower bound, so the point *LOWER* slowly approaches the solution while the point *UPPER* never moves.

When should we stop this iteration? We could continue until a new interval is exactly the same as the previous one—but this might take an impossibly long time. We could continue until the value of $f(x)$ is less than some desired precision ε. This will enable us to solve the problem, Find an x such that $|f(x)|$ is less than ε. It says nothing about how close the solution x is to a zero of $f(x)$. Since the relationship of the size of $f(x)$ to the distance of x from a zero of $f(x)$ depends on the slope of $f(x)$, we could use the slope as our stopping criterion, as shown in Figure 10-4 and described below.

If we approximate the function by the straight line AB between the two points A and B, then the slope of the function is approximated by BC/CA or by QA/QP. Suppose we have just computed the new point Q and want

FIGURE 10-3   Regula falsi method

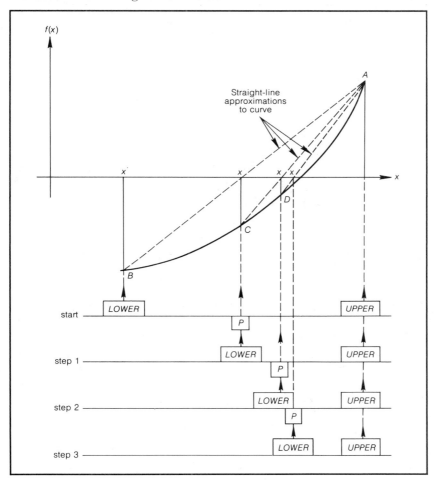

FIGURE 10-4   Using slope as a stopping criterion

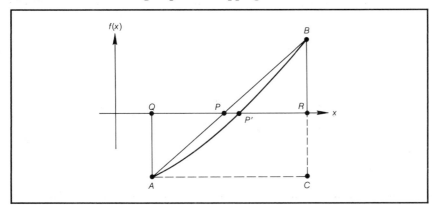

to know whether this is close enough to the solution P'—that is, whether it is within ε of P'. In other words, we want to know whether QP' is less than ε. Since we do not know where P' is, we assume it is close to P and compute QP.

We can compute the distances QA, BC, and CA. They are $-f(q)$, $f(r) - f(q)$, and $r - q$, respectively, where r and q are the x values of R and Q, respectively. From the two forms for the slope we have

$$\frac{BC}{CA} = \frac{QA}{QP}$$

or

$$\frac{f(r) - f(q)}{r - q} = \frac{-f(q)}{QP}$$

That is,

$$QP = -f(q)\frac{r - q}{f(r) - f(q)}$$

We can thus calculate QP and find out whether it is less than ε. If it is, we can stop the iteration. Notice that the following step in the iteration would be to find the point P by approximating the function by the straight line AB. Thus QP is the amount by which we will change the point Q to get the next point P. Hence we are saying that the stopping criterion is to quit the iteration when the change in the estimated solution is less than our desired error ε.

There is no "best" or guaranteed criterion for stopping the iteration. The method just described is the most common, but it can give very poor answers, as the example in Figure 10-5 shows. Because the curve is not

FIGURE 10-5   Poor convergence in regula falsi method

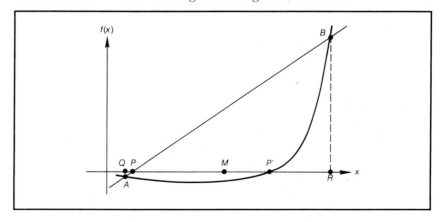

close to the straight-line approximation AB, the point P, although close to Q, is very far from the solution P'.

This example also shows that the regula falsi method can be slower than the bisection method. In Figure 10-5 the bisection method would reduce the interval from QR to MR in one step, whereas the regula falsi method reduces it only from QR to PR. However, both methods are guaranteed to find a solution eventually, since, within rounding errors, the upper and lower bounds always enclose a solution, and at least one endpoint will approach a solution. We say that the bisection and regula falsi methods *converge* to a solution—that is, the computed points get closer to the solution as the iteration proceeds.

10.2 CHORD METHOD

As we have seen, the regula falsi method has the drawback that one of the endpoints may remain a long way from the solution. The function is usually approximated more accurately by a straight line between two points if the points are close together. For this reason, it is worth considering a method similar to the regula falsi method, but in which the last *two* points calculated are kept, as shown in Figure 10-6. The initial pair of points is x_0 and x_1. A straight-line approximation to the function is drawn between $f(x_0)$ and $f(x_1)$, intersecting the x-axis at x_2. The new pair of points is thus x_1 and x_2. The straight line between $f(x_1)$ and $f(x_2)$ intersects the x-axis at x_3, so that the next pair of points is x_2 and x_3. This process continues until some x_n and x_{n+1} are sufficiently close together.

This is called the *chord method*, or *secant method*, because the straight-line approximation is a *chord*, or *secant*, of the graph. Although it is usually faster than the bisection and regula falsi methods, the chord method no longer has the property of convergence, because we cannot guarantee

FIGURE 10-6   Chord method

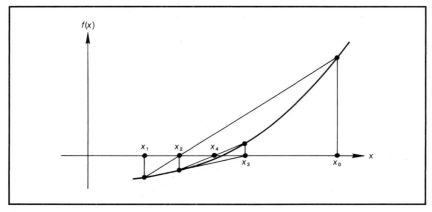

FIGURE 10-7   Nonconvergence in chord method

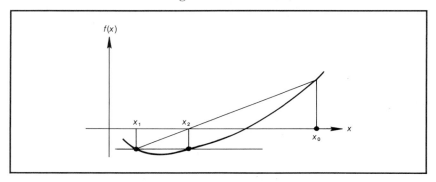

that a solution lies between the currently retained pair of points. An example of nonconvergence is shown in Figure 10-7. The straight-line approximation between the points x_1 and x_2 is parallel to the x-axis, so it does not intersect the axis anywhere. When this happens, we have to "guess" another point and try again. Computer implementations of this method usually try first to use one of the previous points, as in the regula falsi method, or, if that also fails, to move a given fixed amount in alternating directions. However, since convergence cannot be guaranteed, a computer program for the chord method must count the number of iterations attempted and quit if too many are used.

10.3   NEWTON-RAPHSON METHOD

In the chord method we use two previous points to calculate a straight-line approximation to the function. If we know only one point P, at x_0 on the graph, we can calculate a second point P_1 at $x_0 + \Delta$, as shown in Figure 10-8, and pass a straight line through these two points to compute a new approximation x_1. The same process can then be repeated to get the point x_2. This might be called the *quasi-Newton method*.

The line through points P and P_1 in Figure 10-8 is used as an approximation to the curve. As Δ is made smaller, P_1 approaches P and the line through P and P_1 approaches the tangent to the curve at P, as shown in Figure 10-9. In the *Newton-Raphson method*, or *Newton's method*, the tangent itself is used as the approximating line. If the slope of the tangent at point P is S, we have

$$S = \frac{PA}{PB} = \frac{f(x_0)}{x_0 - x_1}$$

Therefore

$$x_0 - x_1 = f(x_0)/S$$

or

$$x_1 = x_0 - f(x_0)/S$$

The general step is given by

$$x_{n+1} = x_n - f(x_n)/S_n \qquad (10.1)$$

where S_n is the slope of the tangent at x_n. To use this method we must be able to calculate both the function $f(x)$ and the slope of its tangent. (Readers who have had calculus will recognize this as the *derivative* of the function.) Consequently the Newton-Raphson method is mainly used for

FIGURE 10-8   Quasi-Newton method

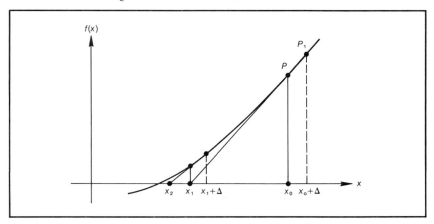

FIGURE 10-9   Newton-Raphson method

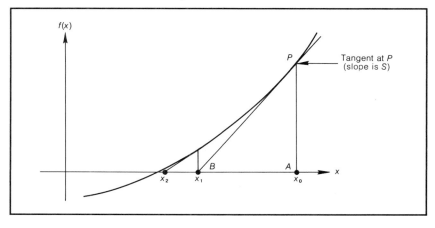

simple functions, such as polynomials, for which methods of calculating the tangent are simple.

A particularly important case is the equation $x^2 - a = 0$. A solution of this equation is $\sqrt{a}$. We used the Newton method to solve this equation in Example 1.4 on page 9. We will now look at it in more detail. The slope of the tangent* of $x^2 - a$ is $2x$. Using this value for S_n in equation (10.1) we get

$$
\begin{aligned}
x_{n+1} &= x_n - \frac{x_n^2 - a}{2x_n} \\
&= \frac{(x_n + a/x_n)}{2}
\end{aligned}
$$

We can show that this particular iteration will always converge, because we have

$$
\begin{aligned}
x_{n+1} - \sqrt{a} &= \frac{x_n^2 + a}{2x_n} - \sqrt{a} \\
&= \frac{(x_n - \sqrt{a})^2}{2x_n}
\end{aligned}
$$

The numerator in the last expression is a square, so it must be nonnegative. Therefore $x_{n+1} - \sqrt{a}$ has the same sign as x_n. Assume that we start

---

*Students who have not had calculus can find the slope as follows: The tangent is the limiting case of a line passing through two points on a curve as the two points get closer and closer. Consider the figure below and the line through the two points P at x and Q at $x + \Delta$.

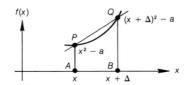

The slope of this line is

$$
\begin{aligned}
S &= \frac{QB - PA}{B - A} = \frac{(x + \Delta)^2 - x^2}{(x + \Delta) - x} \\
&= \frac{x^2 + 2\Delta x + \Delta^2 - x^2}{x + \Delta - x} \\
&= \frac{2\Delta x + \Delta^2}{\Delta} \\
&= 2x + \Delta
\end{aligned}
$$

As Δ gets smaller, the point B approaches the point A and the slope approaches $2x$.

with a positive x_0 and that we take $\sqrt{a}$ to be positive. Then $x_n \geq \sqrt{a} \geq 0$ for all $n \geq 1$. Furthermore, the error in x_{n+1} is

$$x_{n+1} - \sqrt{a} = \frac{(x_n - \sqrt{a})^2}{2x_n} = (x_n - \sqrt{a})\frac{x_n - \sqrt{a}}{2x_n}$$

For $n \geq 1$, $x_n \geq \sqrt{a}$, so that $x_n - \sqrt{a} \leq x_n$. Hence

$$\frac{x_n - \sqrt{a}}{2x_n} \leq \frac{1}{2}$$

Substituting this in the previous equation, we get

$$x_{n+1} - \sqrt{a} \leq \frac{1}{2}(x_n - \sqrt{a})$$

That is, the error in x_{n+1} is no more than 50% of the error in x_n. In fact, the Newton-Raphson method converges very much more rapidly than this. It is one of the fastest methods available for those problems for which it converges, but it is not guaranteed to converge for all problems. (What happens if the slope of the tangent is zero near the solution?) As an illustration of the speed of this method, we show the successive iterates when it is used to compute $\sqrt{2}$ starting with the $x_0 = 1$. In the table below, the computation is carried to nine digits beyond the decimal point.

n	x_n	Error $= x_n - \sqrt{2}$
0	1.000 000 000	−0.414 213 562
1	1.500 000 000	0.085 786 438
2	1.416 666 667	0.002 453 105
3	1.414 215 686	0.000 002 124
4	1.414 213 562	0 (to nine places)

Note that the error between the first and second steps decreases by nearly a factor of 5, much more than our most pessimistic estimate of 2. After that it decreases very rapidly. This is typical of Newton's method: once we are close to the solution, the error decreases extremely rapidly.

PROBLEMS

1 Write a subroutine for the chord method. The parameters to the subroutine should be A, B, X, F, and E, where A and B are the two initial points, F is the function whose zero is to be found, and E is an error tolerance. The iteration should stop when the change in the computed solution in one iteration is less than E. X should be left containing the solution.

2 Consider your solution to Problem 1. Since the stopping criterion may never be satisfied, the subroutine may never terminate. Add another logical parameter, whose value is **true** if a solution is found but **false** if the stopping criterion is not satisfied after 50 iterations.

3 Sketch a function for which the Newton-Raphson method will give a sequence of approximations x_n, each of which is farther from the zero than the last.

11

Iterative Methods for Systems of Linear and Nonlinear Equations

■   ■   ■   ■   ■   ■   ■

Systems of equations arise very frequently in engineering and scientific calculations. The majority of real problems are nonlinear and naturally lead to nonlinear equations. Because nonlinear equations are more difficult to solve than linear equations, we have to consider different types of methods, all iterative. Linear equations are a special case of nonlinear equations, and the methods used for nonlinear equations are also applicable to linear equations. Therefore, while we study methods for nonlinear equations we will also examine their application to linear equations.

In contrast to the case for linear equations, the theory of nonlinear equations cannot in general tell us whether a solution exists or, if there is one, whether it is unique. Consequently, we are often faced with a problem that may or may not have a solution. This means that the program may be searching for a solution that does not exist. In such cases it cannot be successful but must stop for some other reason, such as the use of too much computer time. Because such "escape hatches" are necessary in a program, it is also possible for the program to fail to find a solution in the time available, even though one exists.

Consider the problem mentioned in the introduction to this part of the book:

$$x^2 + y^2 - 2x - 2y - 7 = 0$$
$$x^2 + y^2 + 2x + 2y - 7 = 0$$

In this case we can use formal manipulation techniques to find the solution. (We could also use plane geometry, because these equations represent a pair of circles of radius 3 centered at $(1, 1)$ and $(-1, -1)$, respectively.) If we subtract the first equation from the second we get

$$4x + 4y = 0$$

which tells us that the solutions lie on the straight line $x = -y$. Substituting this relation into either equation to eliminate x gives

$$2y^2 - 7 = 0$$

from which we can compute the solutions directly as $(\sqrt{7/2}, -\sqrt{7/2})$ and $(-\sqrt{7/2}, \sqrt{7/2})$. Although it appears that we can compute the solutions exactly in this case, remember that even the square root cannot be evaluated exactly, so the best we can get is an approximation. A few nonlinear equations can be solved by formal manipulation to reduce them to standard explicit functions involving operations such as the square root for which there are known computational techniques. (There are a number of *symbolic manipulation* programs, including Maxsyma, Reduce, and Formac, that help the user do such manipulation.) However, the majority of nonlinear problems cannot be solved "explicitly," and so must be approached by means of numerical techniques using iterative methods.

Iterative methods are natural for nonlinear problems. One reason for this is that the person with the problem usually does not know whether the problem has several solutions but does know that there should be at least one solution. This is because the problem is usually a mathematical model of some real-world process that has a solution. If the model does not have a solution, it is incorrect and should be changed. The physical basis of the problem usually yields some approximate value of the solution, and this value forms a good first approximation for an iterative process.

In the general nonlinear problem, we have a set of n equations in n unknowns. We ask for the same number of equations as unknowns because we usually expect each equation to determine, in some sense, the value of one of the unknowns. We saw in Chapter 9 that we could often find a unique solution to a system of n linear equations in n unknowns, so we expect a similar situation in some of the cases of nonlinear equations.

Suppose the unknowns are $x_1, x_2, \ldots, x_n$ and the equations are

$$f_1(x_1, x_2, \ldots, x_n) = 0 \qquad (11.1a)$$
$$f_2(x_1, x_2, \ldots, x_n) = 0 \qquad (11.1b)$$
$$\cdots$$
$$f_n(x_1, x_2, \ldots, x_n) = 0 \qquad (11.1c)$$

We often write these in the compact form

$$\mathbf{f}(\mathbf{x}) = 0 \qquad (11.2)$$

where boldface $\mathbf{x}$ stands for the *vector* of the n components x_1 to x_n, and boldface $\mathbf{f}$ stands for the vector of n components f_1 to f_n. In an iterative method we start with an initial approximation. Suppose it is $(x_{1,\,0}, x_{2,\,0}, \ldots, x_{n,\,0})$. How can we improve this approximation? In the previous chapter we saw some methods for solving one nonlinear equation in one unknown. We could use one of these methods to solve one of the above equations for one of the unknowns, using the initial approximation for the values of the other unknowns. For example, we could solve equation (11.1a) for x_1. Since the other values of x_i will still have their first approximation values of $x_{i,\,0}$, we cannot expect the value computed for x_1 by this technique to be the correct solution to the combined system. Let us therefore call it $x_{1,\,1}$—that is, treat it as the next approximation to x_1. If we do this, $x_{1,\,1}$ satisfies

$$f_1(x_{1,\,1}, x_{2,\,0}, \ldots, x_{n,\,0}) = 0 \qquad (11.3)$$

We could solve each of the equations (11.1) for each of the unknowns in this way, so that the new value of x_i is found by solving $f_i(\mathbf{x}) = 0$, using the old values of the other x's. If we call these new values $x_{i,\,1}$, we have a scheme for computing new approximations in terms of the old ones. This scheme can be applied repeatedly, using the relations

$$f_i(x_{1,\,m}, \ldots, x_{i-1,\,m}, x_{i,\,m+1}, x_{i+1,\,m}, \ldots, x_{n,\,m}) = 0 \qquad (11.4)$$

to define the $m + 1$st iterate $\mathbf{x}_{m+1}$) in terms of the mth iterate $\mathbf{x}_m$. Here, $\mathbf{x}_m$ is the vector consisting of the components $x_{1,\,m}, x_{2,\,m}, \ldots, x_{n,\,m}$. Equation (11.4) must be solved n times with $i = 1, \ldots, n$ to get the next iterate, and each solution of this equation involves an iterative process of the type discussed in the previous chapter.

We have suggested a way of computing a new iterate in terms of the old iterate. Is the new one a better solution? Unfortunately it is difficult to answer in general, and there has been a lot of work done, both on simple methods of the above form and on more powerful methods, to specify sufficient conditions under which they will be successful. We will examine this method in a little more detail, not because it is a particularly important method (although there are situations in which it can be useful) but because it illustrates a number of important points.

We can often understand the behavior of a proposed numerical algorithm for nonlinear problems by studying its behavior for linear problems, so let us start by examining this case. When we say that a problem is linear, we mean that the functions involved are linear functions of the unknowns. This means that each of the equations $f_i(\mathbf{x}) = 0$ takes the form

$$s_{i1}x_1 + s_{i2}x_2 + \cdots + s_{in}x_n + r_i = 0 \qquad (11.5)$$

This is a system of n linear equations similar to (9.1), with a replaced with s and b replaced with $-r$. Since at the moment we are only considering the linear case in order to understand what could happen in the nonlinear case, we cannot use the methods of Chapter 9, because we do not know the values of s_{ij} or r_i. We will solve each of the equations (11.5) using one of the iterative methods of the last chapter. However we choose to solve them, when we are done we have obtained the solution that we would get by solving each of the equations in (11.5) directly, namely

$$x_{i,\,m+1} = $$
$$-\frac{s_{i1}x_{1,\,m} + \cdots + s_{i,\,i-1}x_{i-1,\,m} + s_{i,\,i+1}x_{i+1,\,m} + \cdots + s_{in}x_{n,\,m} + r_i}{s_{ii}}$$
$$(11.6)$$

This is simply an iterative method for solving equations (9.1), known as the Jacobi method. The conditions under which it will converge are too technical to discuss here. However, there is an easy-to-apply test to see whether the method will work—a condition that emerges fairly naturally from equation (11.6). Clearly if s_{ii} is zero, (11.6) will cause computational difficulties, and we can expect similar difficulties if s_{ii} is small compared to the other values in the expression. Since we are using the ith equation $f_i(\mathbf{x}) = 0$ to determine x_i, that equation must somehow have a large influence on the value of x_i. If the coefficient of x_i in the ith equation, namely s_{ii}, "dominates" the other coefficients in that equation in the sense that it is larger than the sum of the absolute values of the others, and if this is true for all i, the Jacobi method will converge. This condition is called *diagonal dominance*, because it is a condition on the diagonal of the matrix whose entries are s_{ii}. Formally, it requires that

$$|s_{ii}| \ge |s_{i1}| + |s_{i2}| + \cdots + |s_{1n}|$$

where the s_{ii} term is omitted from the sum on the right-hand side, with inequality for at least one i.

If the method is to converge for nonlinear equations, we must have a related condition—namely, the ith equation must be strongly dependent on the ith unknown.

We stated earlier that the Jacobi method could be used for linear equations. We have seen a perfectly good method for linear equations in Chapter 9, and we might therefore ask why we should use an iterative method that does not always converge. The answer is that iterative methods may be extremely useful for very large problems in which the storage for the matrix of coefficients is a major consideration. Many of the matrices that arise in these problems have very few nonzero entries. Methods for storing these matrices, called *sparse* matrices, are discussed in Section 13.2. For these types of problems, iterative methods can be much more efficient. The Jacobi method and the next iterative method to be discussed are not the best iterative methods to use for linear equations but they are representative of the methods currently in use. The discussion of more advanced methods is beyond the scope of this text.

If we consider computer implementation of the method described by equation (11.6) for linear equations, we see that we need storage for the previous iterate, $\mathbf{x}_m$, while the next one, $\mathbf{x}_{m+1}$, is being computed. Since the execution of the assignment statements equivalent to equation (11.6) typically proceeds sequentially for i from 1 to n, we could consider using a single array of storage for $\mathbf{x}$, updating each entry as its new value is calculated. Then equation (11.6) would become

$$x_{i,\,m+1} = -\frac{s_{i1}x_{1,\,m+1} + \cdots + s_{i,\,i-1}x_{i-1,\,m+1} + s_{i,\,i+1}x_{i+1,\,m} + \cdots + s_{1n}x_{n,\,m} + r_i}{s_{ii}} \tag{11.7}$$

This method, known as the Gauss-Seidel method, uses less storage space than the Jacobi method. Furthermore, for many problems it "converges faster" than the Jacobi method. By this we mean that fewer iterations are needed to achieve the same amount of accuracy. The conditions under which it will converge are difficult to specify precisely; however, it does converge for the condition mentioned above, diagonal dominance of the matrix.

The Gauss-Seidel type of method can be used for nonlinear equations in exactly the same way we use a Jacobi-like method for nonlinear equations. We would progressively solve equations (11.1a), (11.1b), . . ., in turn for x_i, $i = 1, \ldots, n$, using the latest values of the other x's. Each equation could be solved by any convenient method, such as those discussed in the previous chapter.

If we examine the steps used in either the Jacobi or Gauss-Seidel method for nonlinear equations, we see that the code consists of three nested loops. The inner loop iterates to solve a single nonlinear equation, the next loop counts over the n equations, and the outer loop iterates until sufficient accuracy has been obtained. The structure of the program is shown in Program 11-1. This program contains two very vague statements: "`until` . . . `accurate enough`." The determination of sufficient accuracy in an iterative method is a very difficult question, whose answer depends on the context of the problem. For this discussion, we will assume that we iterate until the *residual* of the equation(s) is less than some user-specified error tolerance. The residual of an equation is simply

■ **Program 11.1**   **Jacobi or Gauss-Seidel method for nonlinear equations**

```
Set x to x₀
    repeat
        do for I ← 1 to N
            Set initial approximation to xᵢ
            repeat
                Compute next iterate for xᵢ to solve ith
                equation by some iterative method.
                until xᵢ accurate enough
            enddo
        until x accurate enough
```

the amount by which it is not satisfied. Thus, the residual of $f(x) = 0$ is $f(x)$. This is a suitable definition of "accurate enough" if we are happy with an answer that has a small residual. In that case, it is clear how we terminate the outer loop. What about the inner loop? We could also iterate until the residual of the individual equation was below the user-supplied tolerance. However, in the early steps we are computing only an intermediate iterate, not the final value of x_i, so there seems to be little point in using a lot of computer time to get high accuracy. Instead, we should be content if we can improve the approximation by a modest amount.

The question of how much accuracy to seek in the inner iteration is also a difficult one to answer in general, and we will not examine it further here. Instead, we will assume that we are going to use only one iteration in the inner loop; in other words, we will remove the inner **repeat-until** pair of statements in Program 11-1. Let us now look at the nature of the method used for the inner step. All of the methods described in the last chapter were based on an approximation of the nonlinear function by a straight line. In the case of the regula falsi method and the chord method, the approximation was a *chord* of the function—that is, a straight line joining two points of the curve, as shown in Figure 11-1. In the case of the Newton method, the straight line was the tangent to the curve at a given point. Approximating a function by a straight line is called *linearization*. The chord approximation in Figure 11-1 has the form

$$f(x) \approx f(x_0) + (x - x_0)\frac{f(x_1) - f(x_0)}{x_1 - x_0} \tag{11.8}$$

The expression

$$s = \frac{f(x_1) - f(x_0)}{x_1 - x_0} \tag{11.9}$$

FIGURE 11·1   Chord and tangent

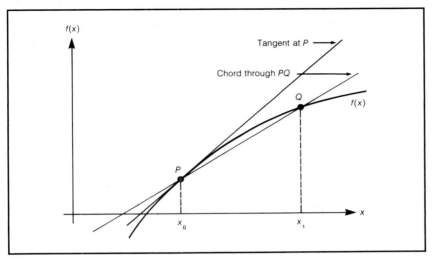

is the slope of the chord. When we discussed the chord method in Chapter 10, x_0 and x_1 were the two most recent iterates. If we use this linearization in Program 11-1, we have to choose some values equivalent to x_0 and x_1 to find the slope of f_i as x_i changes. The current approximation to x_i provides one value. The other can be obtained by *perturbing* x_i by a suitably small amount. Suppose this amount is Δ. This method would then be equivalent to using the expression

$$\frac{f(x_0 + \Delta) - f(x_0)}{\Delta} \tag{11.10}$$

for the slope in place of equation (11.9). As applied in Program 11-1, we would compute the slope of f_i by evaluating

$$\frac{f_i(x_{m,\,i} + \Delta) - f_i(x_{m,\,i})}{\Delta} \tag{11.11}$$

where the values of all other x_j, $j \neq i$, are set to their current values $x_{m,\,j}$ or $x_{m+1,\,j}$, depending on the method being used and the relative values of i and j.

If we were to use the Newton method for the inner loop, we would replace this slope approximation by the slope of the tangent. As mentioned in Chapter 10, this can be found by differentiation. Some software may require the user to provide subroutines to evaluate not only $f_i(\mathbf{x})$ but also the slope of the tangent. However, it may be difficult or impossible for the user to compute the tangent slope directly. Since the tangent slope is defined as the limit of the value (11.11) as Δ approaches zero, the user could try to approximate it with equation (11.11), using a suitably small Δ. This brings us back to the use of a chord method, which is why a chord method is sometimes called a quasi-Newton method.

If we are going to linearize f_i with respect to x_i—that is, to approximate it by a linear function in x_i—why not approximate it by a linear function in all of the x_j? Suppose we want a linear function in all x_j that is equal to f_i at a particular value of $\mathbf{x}$, say $\mathbf{x}_m$. We will get a function of the form

$$f_i(\mathbf{x}) \approx f_i(\mathbf{x}_m) + s_{i1}(x_1 - x_{m,1}) + \cdots + s_{in}(x_n - x_{m,n}) \quad (11.12)$$

where s_{ij} is the slope of the approximation to f_i with respect to the jth variable x_j. You can visualize the meaning of slope if you think of a hill whose height is a function of two variables, longitude and latitude, or x and y. The slope of the hill with respect to x is a measure of how fast the height changes as one moves in the x direction, and similarly for the y direction. If we approximate all of the functions by this linearization, we have a set of linear equations to which the methods of Chapter 9 can be applied directly. Now the program takes the form shown in Program 11-2. The only question concerns the way in which the linearization is formed. If the tangent directions are used, we call this the Newton method for systems of equations. It is known that Newton's method converges rapidly for many reasonably behaved systems of equations, provided that the initial approximation is sufficiently close to the solution.

If the linearization in Program 11-2 is formed by approximating the slopes by means of chords, the method is called a quasi-Newton method. It does not usually converge as rapidly as the Newton method, but it may be easier to program.

Because these methods cannot be guaranteed to converge, a practical program must take many precautions to avoid needless use of computer time. Usually a code will use other methods until it has an approximation in the neighborhood of a solution, after which it will switch to a Newton-like method. In general, the user is advised to look in the program library for a subroutine to solve these equations rather than to write his or her own code.

■ **Program 11.2   Solution of nonlinear equations by linearization**

```
Set x to x₀
   repeat
      Form linearization approximation for
      equations about current iterate and solve for
      new iterate, x, using Gaussian elimination.
      until x accurate enough
```

PROBLEMS

1 Program a Jacobi method to solve the 10 equations

$$2x_1 - x_2 = 1$$
$$-x_1 + 2x_2 - x_3 = 0$$
$$-x_2 + 2x_3 - x_4 = 0$$
$$-x_3 + 2x_4 - x_5 = 0$$
$$\cdots$$
$$-x_8 + 2x_9 - x_{10} = 0$$
$$-x_9 + 2x_{10} = 0$$

Execute your program starting with an initial approximation of 0 for all 10 x_i. Continue execution until the largest residual (that is, the largest amount by which any one of the equations is not satisfied) is less than 0.01. After every iteration, print the ratio of the largest residual to the largest residual after the previous iteration.

2 Repeat the previous problem using the Gauss-Seidel method.

12

Numerical
Errors

■　　　■　　　■　　　■　　　■　　　■　　　■

In this chapter we take a brief look at *numerical errors*. A better word for them would be "inaccuracies," because they are in no sense the same as program errors. Numerical errors unavoidably arise in some calculations; although many programmers would claim that program errors are unavoidable, they represent mistakes by a person. Unfortunately, not all numerical errors in calculation are unavoidable; a numerical error that could have been avoided also represents a mistake by a person and is as much of a sin as a program error! At this level we cannot study numerical errors in much detail; their general analysis is an advanced branch of mathematics called *numerical analysis*. In this book we will simply look at the ways in which they can arise and try to see some of the obvious pitfalls. Perhaps the most important lesson to be learned from this chapter is that the computer is not infallible, even when the program is "correct" from the point of view of the operations performed. Even if you are not particularly concerned with numerical computations, you should be aware of the traps awaiting the unwary.

Numerical errors initially arise from two sources. The first source is called *rounding error*, and is due to the fact that only a finite subset of all the real numbers can be represented in the computer as floating-point numbers. Therefore we must approximate most input data and the results of most arithmetic operations. The second source of numerical error is called *truncation error*. It has nothing to do with the use of truncation as a means of converting real numbers to representable floating-point numbers, but refers to the approximation of functions that can be computed exactly only by an infinite sequence of operations. For example, sin(y) is given by the series

$$y - \frac{y^3}{3!} + \frac{y^5}{5!} - \frac{y^7}{7!} + \cdots$$

If a finite number of terms of this series are used to compute sin(y), the error due to truncating the series is called the truncation error. The errors introduced by rounding and truncation are initially small, but sometimes their effect is amplified by subsequent operations.

12.1 ERRORS IN ARITHMETIC [ROUNDING ERROR]

Arithmetic error arises when initial data or intermediate results cannot be represented exactly in the computer. Because machines are usually more precise than we are, we often assume that the computer is precise enough for anything we need to do. Suppose that memory carries only five digits of precision in floating point. Since numbers we measure in experiments are seldom accurate to more than three digits, surely five are sufficient? Besides, most actual computers carry from seven to sixteen digits of precision. Surely that is enough, even if our experimental data is good to six digits? Often it is, but we must be aware that things can go wrong.

The number of digits of precision carried in floating point is fixed. The *weight* of these digits varies with the exponent of the number. Thus if a number is rounded to put it in the form

$$\pm .nnnnn \times 10^e$$

the rounding error will be a maximum of $\pm 0.000005 \times 10^e$. Its actual value will depend on the exponent e. When an arithmetic operation results in an answer that cannot be represented exactly, additional rounding errors are introduced. These depend on the exponent of the answer.

Example 12.1
Rounding Errors

A common example of the buildup of rounding errors is in the repeated addition of the same number to a running total. Suppose that in the nth pass through a program loop we need the value $n/6$. One way of arranging

TABLE 12-1   Running Sum of 1/6

Pass	Sum Correctly Rounded	Sum Truncated	True Answer Rounded
1	$.17 \times 10^0$	$.16 \times 10^0$	$.17 \times 10^0$
2	$.34 \times 10^0$	$.32 \times 10^0$	$.33 \times 10^0$
3	$.51 \times 10^0$	$.48 \times 10^0$	$.50 \times 10^0$
4	$.68 \times 10^0$	$.64 \times 10^0$	$.67 \times 10^0$
5	$.85 \times 10^0$	$.80 \times 10^0$	$.83 \times 10^0$
6	$.10 \times 10^1$	$.96 \times 10^0$	$.10 \times 10^1$
7	$.12 \times 10^1$	$.11 \times 10^1$	$.12 \times 10^1$
8	$.14 \times 10^1$	$.12 \times 10^1$	$.13 \times 10^1$
9	$.16 \times 10^1$	$.13 \times 10^1$	$.15 \times 10^1$
10	$.18 \times 10^1$	$.14 \times 10^1$	$.17 \times 10^1$
11	$.20 \times 10^1$	$.15 \times 10^1$	$.18 \times 10^1$
12	$.22 \times 10^1$	$.16 \times 10^1$	$.20 \times 10^1$

this is to initialize a variable to 1/6 and add 1/6 to it after each pass. In order to see what happens after only a few passes, let us consider the behavior of a machine with only two significant digits of precision in floating point. One-sixth is represented by 0.17×10^0 with rounding, by 0.16×10^0 with truncation.

Let us look at the state of the variable in the first 12 passes in each case. They are shown in Table 12-1. Once the total reaches 1.0, future additions of 1/6 can only add 0.1 or 0.2, because the intermediate result has an exponent of 1. If the passes through the loop continued until the total was 10, further additions would not change the result, since 10 + 0.16 is still 10 to two significant digits. It is true that modern computers have more than two significant digits, but it is also true that we often make more than 12 passes through a loop.

One way to overcome this phenomenon is to form an integer N that is equal to the number of passes through the loop and divide that by 6. It takes a little more computer time, since division is slower than addition, but it is much more accurate, because the maximum error is a rounding error in the last significant digit of the answer. This example demonstrates that the fastest program may not be the most accurate.

As Example 12.1 shows, rounding errors can accumulate to the point that the answer is meaningless. If that were the only way rounding errors could become significant, the analysis of numerical error would be relatively easy. Unfortunately, if we allow intermediate results to become large, they will include large rounding errors. If the errors remain the same size when they are transmitted to the solution, the answer will be lost in the error.

Large rounding errors are transmitted to the answer when two large numbers of almost the same size are subtracted. This phenomenon is known as *cancellation*. Consider, for example, the problem of subtracting 129/388 from 162/485. The correct answer is 3/1940. If the numbers are correctly rounded to five significant digits, the arithmetic process yields

$$0.33402 \times 10^0 - 0.33247 \times 10^0 = 0.15500 \times 10^{-2}$$

whereas the answer, correctly rounded to five digits, is 0.15464×10^{-2}. (See Figure 12-1.) What has happened? When the fractions were represented to five-digit precision, rounding errors were introduced. The true value of 129/388 is 0.3324742 . . ., so a rounding error of 0.0000042 . . . $\times 10^0$ is made. Similarly, a rounding error of 0.0000006 . . . $\times 10^0$ is made in representing 162/485 to five digits. When these two numbers are subtracted, their first two digits cancel, decreasing the exponent of the result by 2. The total rounding error is $(0.0000006 - 0.0000042) \times 10^0$, which is $(-0.00036) \times 10^{-2}$, and so it shows up as early as the fourth place of the answer. However, the error is not *caused* by cancellation; it is only uncovered by cancellation. The error occurred when the numbers were rounded. At that time the error was in the sixth significant place; cancellation moved it to a more significant position.

A well-known example of cancellation is the addition of three numbers. Suppose we form A + B + C in five-digit floating-point arithmetic by first adding A to B, then adding C to the result. Suppose the values of A, B, and C are -0.12344×10^0, $+ 0.12345 \times 10^0$, and $+0.32741 \times 10^{-4}$, re-

FIGURE 12-1   Cancellation

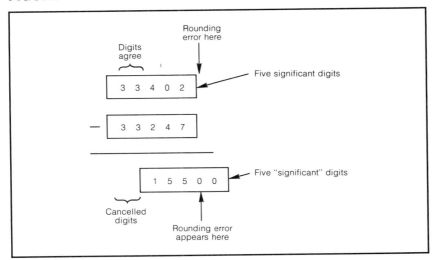

spectively. $A + B$ is 0.00001×10^0, or 0.10000×10^{-4} after normalization. When C is added to this, we get 0.42741×10^{-4}. Suppose, on the other hand, we first add C to B, then add the result to A. $B + C$ is 0.123482741×10^0, which is 0.12348×10^0 after rounding. When A is added to this, we get 0.00004×10^0, which is 0.40000×10^{-4} after normalization. Thus the result (0.42741×10^{-4} or 0.40000×10^{-4}) is dependent on the order of the arithmetic. Although exact addition is *associative*—that is, $(A + B) + C = A + (B + C)$—the result of machine computation may not be.

Example 12.2
Variance Calculation

If the N numbers in a set are $S(1), S(2), \ldots, S(N)$, then their *mean* (or *average*) is

$$A = (S(1) + S(2) + \cdots + S(N))/N$$

and their *variance* is

$$V = ((S(1) - A)^2 + (S(2) - A)^2 + \cdots + (S(N) - A)^2)/N$$

The variance is a measure of the scattering of a set of values. If all the values are the same, the variance is zero. The mean and variance can be calculated from the above formulas using two loops, the first to calculate the mean by summing the values and the second to calculate the variance by summing $(S(1) - A)^2$. This takes $2N - 2$ additions, N subtractions, N multiplications, and 2 divisions. Alternatively, we can rewrite V as

$$
\begin{aligned}
V &= ((S(1)^2 - 2S(1) \times A + A^2) + \cdots \\
&\quad + (S(N)^2 - 2S(N) \times A + A^2))/N \\
&= (S(1)^2 + S(2)^2 + \cdots + S(N)^2)/N - 2 \times A \\
&\quad \times (S(1) + S(2) + \cdots + S(N))/N \\
&\quad + (A^2 + A^2 + \cdots + A^2)/N
\end{aligned}
$$

The second term contains $(S(1) + S(2) + \cdots + S(N))/N$, which is exactly A, while the last contains N instances of A^2. Hence

$$
\begin{aligned}
V &= (S(1)^2 + S(2)^2 + \cdots + S(N)^2)/N - 2 \times A \times A + A^2 \\
&= (S(1)^2 + S(2)^2 + \cdots + S(N)^2)/N - A^2
\end{aligned}
$$

A program to compute this is shown in Program 12-1.

```
VAR: subprogram (S,N)
```
The value of this function is the variance of the N values in the real array S.
```
    integer I,N
    real VAR,S(N),V,A
        V ← 0.0
        A ← 0.0
        do for I ← 1 to N
```
Form sum in A and sum of squares in V.
```
            A ← A + S(I)
            V ← V + S(I)↑2
            enddo
        A ← A/FLOAT(N)
        V ← V/FLOAT(N) − A↑2
        return (V)
    endsubprogram VAR
```

This approach requires $N - 1$ fewer subtractions and only one more multiplication than the earlier method, and uses only one loop, resulting in a faster program. However, if the average (A) is large but the variance (V) is small, this faster method may be much less accurate. Consider an example using a three-digit computer that rounds correctly. Suppose we wish to find the variance of the five numbers 4.3, 4.4, 4.5, 4.6, and 4.7. Using the earlier method, we first sum them to get 22.5. On dividing by 5 we get the correct average of 4.5. No rounding errors are introduced if three digits are used. Next we calculate the sum of the squares of the differences, as shown in Table 12-2. The computed variance is $0.1 \times 10^0/5 = 0.2 \times 10^{-1}$. Again there are no rounding errors, so the answer is exact. By contrast, the second method will square each of the S(I)'s and round the answers to three digits. This process and the total are shown in

TABLE 12-2   Variance Calculation by Slow Method

$(4.3 - 4.5)^2$		$= 0.4 \times 10^{-1}$
$(4.4 - 4.5)^2$		$= 0.1 \times 10^{-1}$
$(4.5 - 4.5)^2$		$= 0.0$
$(4.6 - 4.5)^2$		$= 0.1 \times 10^{-1}$
$(4.7 - 4.5)^2$		$= 0.4 \times 10^{-1}$
Total		$= 0.1 \times 10^0$
Variance =	Total/5	$= 0.2 \times 10^{-1}$

TABLE 12-3 Variance Calculation by Fast Method

I	$S(I)$	$S(I)^2$	Rounded to Three Digits	Sum So Far, Rounded to Three Digits
1	4.3	18.49	18.5	$18.5 = S(1)^2$
2	4.4	19.36	19.4	$37.9 = S(1)^2 + S(2)^2$
3	4.5	20.25	20.3	$58.2 = S(1)^2 + S(2)^2 + S(3)^2$
4	4.6	21.16	21.2	$79.4 = \cdots$
5	4.7	22.09	22.1	$102. = \cdots$

Variance = Sum/5 $- 20.3 = 0.1 \times 10^0$

Table 12-3. This time we calculate V using three-digit rounded arithmetic, to get

$$V = \frac{102.}{5} - (4.5)^2 = 20.4 - 20.3 = 0.1$$

This is in error by 400%! An extreme example, yes—but one to remind you that the fastest way is not always the best.

12.2 TRUNCATION ERROR

Truncation error arises because an infinite process necessary to compute a function must be truncated after a finite number of steps. We have already mentioned the example of $\sin(y)$. Many of the simple functions are given by power series. For example

$$\exp(y) = 1 + y + \frac{y^2}{2!} + \frac{y^3}{3!} + \cdots$$

If we want to know how many terms to use, we must decide how much precision we need and the range of y to be allowed. If, for example, we are interested in $-1 \le y \le 1$, the difference between $\exp(y)$ and $1 + y + \cdots + y^n/n!$ is certainly less than

$$E_n = \frac{1}{(n+1)!} + \frac{1}{(n+2)!} + \cdots$$

Since

$$1 + 1 + \frac{1}{2!} + \frac{1}{3!} + \cdots = e = 2.7182818 \ldots$$

TABLE 12-4 Values of Maximum Error in Approximation to exp(y)

n	2	3	4	5
E_n	0.218 . . .	0.0516 . . .	0.00995 . . .	0.00161 . . .

we can calculate the maximum error for various n to be

$$E_n = 2.7182818 \ldots - \left(1 + 1 + \frac{1}{2!} + \cdots + \frac{1}{n!}\right)$$

Values of E_n are shown in Table 12-4. A person designing a function procedure for exp could pick a value of n from a table such as this. (Not all functions can be treated this simply.)

Even if computer arithmetic were infinitely accurate, stopping the calculation of a series after a finite number of terms would lead to truncation error. This type of error also occurs in some of the other examples we have discussed. The method of bisection, for example, computes more accurate approximations to the solution of an equation by moving the upper and lower bounds closer together. But no matter how much accuracy is achieved in the arithmetic or how many steps are taken, the two bounds will always be separate, so we will not get an exact answer unless we are lucky and happen to hit the answer when one of the midpoints is formed.

12.3 AMPLIFICATION OF ERRORS

Most problems start with data that contains errors. These may come, for example, from incorrect measurement in experiments. Obviously, errors in the data will lead to errors in the answers. Rounding and truncation error also lead to errors in the answers. Even though all such errors are of limited size—for example, less than 0.1%—it does not follow that the errors in the final answer will be similarly restricted in size. Indeed, in the examples above, the final errors were much larger, because of large intermediate results. Even in methods of solution that involve no truncation error and in which arithmetic is done with arbitrary accuracy, errors in the initial data can be magnified out of all proportion.

Such problems are said to be *ill-conditioned*. In an ill-conditioned problem, no method can lead to an accurate answer, so we cannot come up with a solution to the difficulty. However, it is important to know when ill-conditioning can arise, so that we will know when our answers are nonsense.

An example of an ill-conditioned problem is that of deciding where a moon-bound rocket is going to land, assuming that it is aimed from the earth and that no midcourse corrections are allowed. The effect on the final destination of errors in the initial angle and velocity is critical, since a small variation will leave the rocket wandering in space or crashing into the sun, 1.5×10^8 kilometers off course!

In this section we will start with a simple example of an ill-conditioned problem. We will then investigate a method of solution of a problem that is initially well-conditioned but can be changed into an ill-conditioned problem if care is not exercised. In this case a good problem is ruined by a poor choice in the method of solution.

Consider the following system of two equations in two unknowns:

$$0.992u + 0.873v = 0.119$$
$$0.481u + 0.421v = 0.060 \tag{12.1}$$

These can be seen by inspection to have the solution $u = 1$, $v = -1$. Suppose these numbers are the result of measurements in an experiment and are good only to within ± 0.001. Thus the right-hand side of the first equation might be 0.120 rather than 0.119. Let us solve the *perturbed* problem

$$0.992u + 0.873v = 0.120$$
$$0.481u + 0.421v = 0.060 \tag{12.2}$$

The answers are

$$u = 0.815$$
$$v = -0.789$$

to three digits, about a 20% change caused by a 1% change in the problem. It is easy to construct examples in which the change in the answer is arbitrarily large. For example

$$0.400y + 0.400z = 0.800$$
$$0.401y + 0.400z = 0.801 \tag{12.3}$$

has the solution $y = z = 1$, whereas

$$0.400y + 0.400z = 0.800$$
$$0.401y + 0.400z = 0.800 \tag{12.4}$$

has the solution $y = 0$, $z = 2$. A change of one part in 800 gives a 100% change in the answer!

FIGURE 12-2   Graph of $0.400y + 0.400z = 0.800$

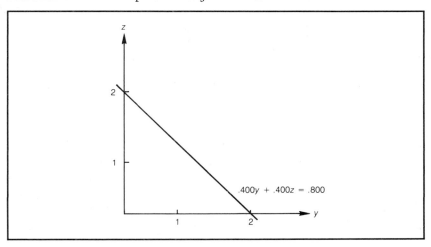

FIGURE 12-3   Region of solution

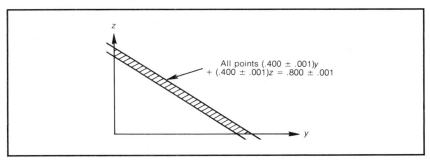

What is happening in these examples? A pictorial representation makes it clear. The set of values of y and z for which

$$0.400y + 0.400z = 0.800$$

forms a line on a graph of y versus z, as shown in Figure 12-2. This line represents all those points (y, z) that satisfy the first of equations (12.3). If we recognize that the initial data has errors, so that the equation might really be $0.400y + 0.400z = 0.801$, we see that points on this perturbed line could equally well satisfy the first equation *within the accuracy we were able to measure*. When we consider all possible equations that could replace the first one if we allowed each of the coefficients to be perturbed by any amount up to its maximum error, we see that the set of points that

FIGURE 12-4   Solution of a pair of equations

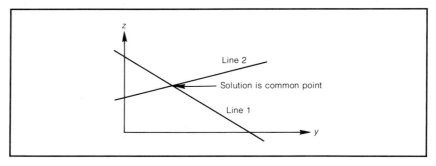

satisfy the first equation (or rather, satisfy what we know about it) forms a region like the "thick line"* shown in Figure 12-3.

The second equation also represents a line if the coefficients are known exactly (see Figure 12-4), or a "thick line" if there are errors in the coefficients. The solution of a pair of equations, each of which is known exactly, is the point of intersection of two lines, as shown in Figure 12-4. When we allow for error, a possible solution will be any point in the common region, as shown in Figure 12-5. It is not possible to determine y and z more precisely than shown if the given data is approximate. This is all right if the lines are only about 0.004 thick and oriented as shown. The uncertainty in y and z is only about 0.007. However, suppose the two

---

*We describe the region as a thick line for convenience. However, it is not a strip with parallel sides, since it includes lines with slightly different slopes. For example, it includes

$$0.399y + 0.401z = 0.800 \pm 0.001$$

and

$$0.401y + 0.399z = 0.800 \pm 0.001$$

We can compute the thickness of the region at various points as follows. Near the center of Figure 12-3 at $y = 1$, we determine z from

$$(0.400 \pm 0.001)z = 0.800 \pm 0.001 - (0.400 \pm 0.001)y$$

with $y = 1$. This means that z lies between $0.398/0.401 = 0.9925$ and $0.402/0.399 = 1.0075$. Hence, the uncertainty in z is 0.015. At $y = 10$ a similar calculation shows that z lies in $(-3.200 \pm 0.011)/(0.400 \pm 0.001)$, or between $-3.189/0.401 = -7.95$ and $-3.211/0.399 = -8.05$, for an uncertainty of about 0.10. At $y = 100$ we can compute a range for z of -97.5 to -98.5 for an uncertainty of 1.0. Hence, the thick line gets thicker as y (and z) get larger, reflecting the fact that the *absolute* uncertainty is proportional to the size of the numbers involved, while the *relative* uncertainty—that is, its size relative to the size of z—is roughly constant.

lines are nearly parallel, as shown in Figure 12-6. In that case, the common region is very large, even though the lines are not very thick—that is, even though the initial data is fairly accurate. The examples we gave above both represented nearly parallel lines. Nothing can be done to determine the answer more accurately than it is determined by the original problem. If the answer is very sensitive to changes in the original data, the problem is ill-conditioned.

However, we can hope to determine a solution that lies in the region common to the two "thick lines," or at least close to both of the original lines. That is to say, we should be able to solve a problem that is no more than a small perturbation of the original problem. If we do and the problem is well-conditioned, the computed solution will be close to the correct solution. If the problem is ill-conditioned, the computed solution may not be close to the correct solution, but it will be no worse than the solution to a "nearby" problem—and since the original data may well

FIGURE 12-5   Area of possible solution

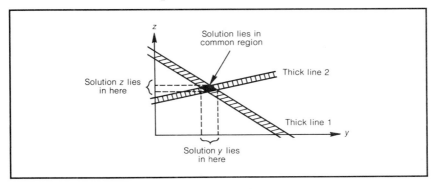

FIGURE 12-6   Area of possible solution with nearly parallel lines

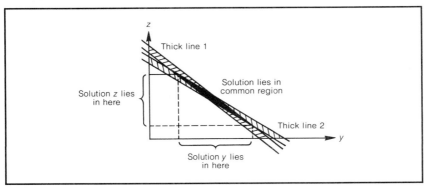

have been in error, the solution to the real problem could be equally far from the solution of the problem solved as is the computed solution.

If we are given a well-conditioned problem, we should be able to determine the answers accurately; but sometimes a bad choice of method will make the solution very sensitive to rounding or truncation error, or even to errors in the initial values. This is particularly true in solving linear equations. Let us consider an example using three-digit floating-point arithmetic:

$$0.512y - 0.920 \times 10^{-3}z = 0.511$$
$$0.117 \times 10^{-2}y + 0.648z = 0.649 \tag{12.5}$$

The two lines represented are almost at right angles, so the problem is well-conditioned. (The answer is $y = z = 1$ to three digits.) The usual method of solution is to use the first equation to express the first variable (y) in terms of the other variables. In this case we divide the first equation by 0.512 to get

$$y - 0.180 \times 10^{-2}z = 0.998 \tag{12.6}$$

and then subtract 0.117×10^{-2} times equation (12.6) from the second of equations (12.5) to get z. Thus we have

$$\frac{0.117 \times 10^{-2}y + 0.648z}{-0.117 \times 10^{-2}(y - 0.180 \times 10^{-2}z)} = \frac{0.649}{-0.117 \times 10^{-2} \times 0.998}$$

If we do this arithmetic rounded to three digits we get

$$0.648z = 0.648$$

or $z = 1.00$. Equation (12.6) then tells us that

$$y = 0.998 + 0.180 \times 10^{-2} = 1.00$$

to three digits. Suppose, however, that we had written equations (12.5) in the reverse order:

$$0.117 \times 10^{-2}y + 0.648z = 0.649$$
$$0.512y - 0.920 \times 10^{-3}z = 0.511 \tag{12.7}$$

We divide the first of equations (12.7) by 0.117×10^{-2} to get

$$y + 554z = 555 \tag{12.8}$$

Now we subtract 0.512 times equation (12.8) from the second of equations (12.7) to get rid of y:

$$\frac{0.512y - 0.920 \times 10^{-3}z}{-0.512(y + 554z)} = \frac{0.511}{-0.512 \times 555}$$

In three-digit rounded arithmetic we get

$$-284z = -283$$

or

$$z = 0.996$$

Substituting this into equation (12.8) we find

$$y = 555 - 554 \times 0.996 = 555 - 552 = 3.00$$

The answer for z is reasonable (0.4% error, which is all we can expect in view of the initial error). The answer for y is hopeless, and yet the problems is well-conditioned. What has happened? The answer is that we have turned it into an ill-conditioned problem in the middle of the solution by making a bad choice of which equation to handle first. Small rounding errors then perturb the solution of this new ill-conditioned problem. Again we can see what is happening by using a graphical interpretation.

When we divide an equation to make the coefficient of one of the variables equal to 1, we do not change the line it represents, so this step has little effect. When we subtract a multiple of one equation from another, we get a third equation, which also represents a straight line. Any values of y and z that lie on both of the original lines must also lie on this third line, since if both of the original equations are satisfied, so is the third. Hence this line passes through the intersection of the other two, as shown in Figure 12-7. We can replace the problem of finding the common point of line 1 and line 2 by that of finding the common point of lines 1 and 3. We chose line 3 so that y did not appear in its equation: hence it is parallel to the y axis. In Figure 12-7, line 1 is nearly vertical, so our new problem appears to be well-conditioned.

In equations (12.5), the first equation corresponds to a nearly vertical

FIGURE 12-7   Effect of elimination of variable

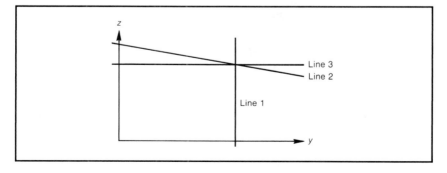

FIGURE 12-8   Regions of uncertainty

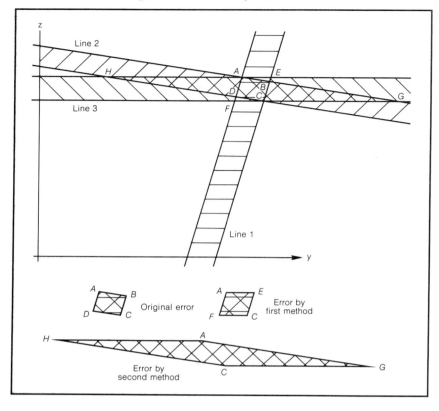

line, the second to a nearly horizontal line. When we eliminate y from the second equation to get a horizontal line, we still have lines nearly at right angles, so we still have a well-conditioned problem. However, when we reverse the order and keep the second and third lines by eliminating the first equation, we give ourselves an ill-conditioned problem. This is shown with "thick lines" in Figure 12-8. The original region of uncertainty is $ABCD$. Line 3 must contain this region, since any solution of the original problem must lie in the thick line 3. If lines 1 and 3 are now used to find the solution, the minimum region of uncertainty is $AECF$; if lines 2 and 3 are used, the region is much larger—namely, $AGCH$.

In a large system of equations, similar problems can arise. One indication of potential trouble occurs when a pivot element is small. Referring back to Program 9-1a, we see that the diagonal element A(I, I) is selected as the pivot and will be used to eliminate all elements below A(I, I) in column I. If A(I, I) is small compared to an element to be eliminated, say A(J, I), then other elements in row J may be increased greatly when the program subtracts A(J, I) / A(I, I) times row I

from row J. If the elements in row J become large, they will be subject to large rounding errors, which will later be revealed by cancellation. We can see this process in equation (12-8). The coefficients have become large, so when the value of z is substituted, cancellation occurs, revealing the error.

It is difficult to avoid some amplification of error in this problem. The solution usually employed is *partial pivoting*. In this technique, the rows of the problem are exchanged as necessary to make `A(I,I)` the largest of the elements `A(K,I)`, for K from I to N, before the Ith pivot is chosen. This process was implemented in Program 9-1e. A better process is called *full pivoting*. In full pivoting, the largest of the elements `A(J, K)`, for J and K from I to N, is chosen as the pivot. `A(J,K)` can be moved into the (I, I) position by interchanging rows I and J and columns I and K. Interchanging rows has no effect; interchanging columns means that the variables are associated with different columns. Full pivoting is seldom used, because the resulting program is slower.

PROBLEMS

1 What is rounding error?

2 What is cancellation?

3 How can cancellation magnify the effect of rounding error in the final answer?

4 What is truncation error?

5 Compute the mean and variance of the numbers 4.9, 5.05, 4.98, 4.89, and 5.02 using correctly rounded three-digit arithmetic by the techniques used in Tables 12-2 and 12-3.

6 What is an ill-conditioned problem?

7 Is the problem of computing the hypotenuse of a right triangle, given the other two sides, well-conditioned?

8 Solve the equations

$$-0.263a + 0.527b = 0.392$$
$$0.826a + 0.412b = 0.851$$

by hand, using three-digit rounded floating-point arithmetic.

9 Solve the equations

$$0.215x + 0.430y = 0.258$$
$$0.461x + 0.817y = 0.553$$

by hand, using three-digit rounded floating-point arithmetic. Are your answers accurate? Is the problem well-conditioned?

10 a. Modify Programs 9-1a to 9-1e to use full pivoting. You should use an array of N integers to record which column of A is used for the Ith pivot. If this array is `COLUMN`, it should be set initially so that

COLUMN(I) = I for *I* from 1 to *N*. If, when the *I*th pivot is being selected, the *K*th column is used, the *I*th and *K*th elements in COLUMN should be switched. All columns of A should be referenced through COLUMN. That is, to find the *I*th column of A, we write A(J,COLUMN(I)) for *J* from 1 to *N*.

b. If this is done, how do we find the solution for x_i when the program has finished execution?

P A R T

IV

DATA
STRUCTURES

■   ■   ■   ■

All data has structure, and the representation and manipulation of that structure is an important part of an algorithm. For example, in a binary search on an ordered table it is necessary to read to the middle entry of the part of the table remaining to be searched. This means that the information must be stored in such a way that it is easy to get to that point rapidly, or the implementation of the algorithm will be very inefficient. If we need to update information during the process of executing a program, we must store the information in such a way that the update can be done rapidly, or we will again suffer a loss of efficiency.

In Part I we examined searching and sorting in several fundamental data structures: arrays, lists, and trees. A *list* is a linear (that is, sequential) arrangement of elements. It can be stored as a one-dimensional array, but this method makes the task of inserting and deleting entries tedious. The most flexible way of storing a list was seen to be as a chain of *nodes*, with each node pointing to the next. Thus a list is characterized as containing one single path connecting all the nodes, as shown in Figure IV-1. If each node in the list consists of one pointer and some data, it is a *one-way list* like the one in Figure IV-1a.

In some applications it is desirable to be able to move through the list in both directions. This requires two pointers in each node, one pointing to the preceding and

FIGURE IV-1   Lists

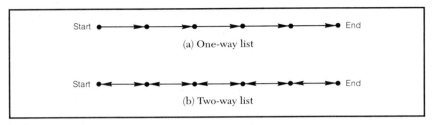

Start ●————▶● ———▶● ———▶● ———▶● ————▶● End

(a) One-way list

Start ●◀————▶●◀———▶●◀———▶●◀———▶●◀———▶● End

(b) Two-way list

one to the following node. The result is a *two-way list* such as that in Figure IV-1b. One-way lists are also called *directed lists*, and two-way lists are called *undirected lists*. The form of list we use depends on the application.

We found that a single path was inadequate for some applications, so we introduced *tree* structures. Whereas a list contains only a single path from one node to the next with no branching, a tree can have several branches from a given node. It is restricted, however, to one and only one path between any two nodes. (In our earlier discussion we restricted ourselves further to *binary trees*, which can have no more than three branches at any node: one coming in from above and no more than two leaving to nodes below. We will discuss more general trees later.)

In this part we will examine some more general data structures and ways of representing information, and apply these to some important examples.

13

Graphs

■ ■ ■ ■ ■ ■ ■

A *graph* is simply a collection of nodes and branches in which each branch links one node to another (including, possibly, to itself). An example of a graph is a road map: if each road junction is called a node, then each road is a branch. An *undirected* graph is a graph in which there is no particular direction associated with a branch; if there is, the graph is a *directed* graph (or *digraph* for short). Thus a road map in which every road is one-way would be a digraph.

Figure 13-1 shows some examples of graphs. Several other features of graphs are illustrated in this figure. In Figure 13-1b we see that there can be more than one branch between two nodes (nodes B and D in this example) and that a node can be connected to itself (as node A is). We can also see that there need not be any path between two nodes (node E cannot be reached from node B). Such a graph is called *unconnected*. Normally we deal with *connected* graphs. Figure 13-1c shows a directed graph that is connected. Again, there can be several branches between two nodes in either direction. Notice, however, that there is no way to go from D to C, or from C to A, following the direction of the branches.

FIGURE 13-1   Examples of graphs

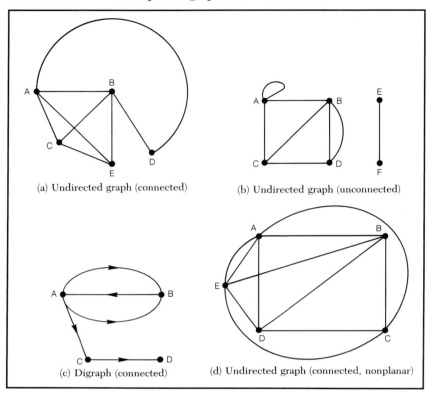

(a) Undirected graph (connected)

(b) Undirected graph (unconnected)

(c) Digraph (connected)

(d) Undirected graph (connected, nonplanar)

In Figures 13-1a and 13-1d we see branches crossing. There is no significance to the positions of the nodes and the branches; a graph displays only the connections between the nodes—that is, the *topology* of the system. We could redraw Figure 13-1a as shown in Figure 13-2. It is the same graph but now has no crossings. A graph that can be so drawn is called a *planar* graph, because it can be drawn on a plane. (Before the advent of freeways with their overpasses, all road maps were planar graphs.) Figure 13-1d is an example of a *nonplanar* graph. There is no way of drawing it on a plane without branches crossing.

A graph may have data associated with either the nodes, the branches, or both. For example, the name of the junction (town, if the only junctions are at towns), population, and elevation are all examples of data that could be associated with the nodes of a road map. Distance, average driving time, and vertical climb or fall are examples of data that could be associated with the branches.

There are many problems in which graph structures are of interest. We will investigate one problem in detail in the example below.

FIGURE 13-2   Figure 13-1a redrawn

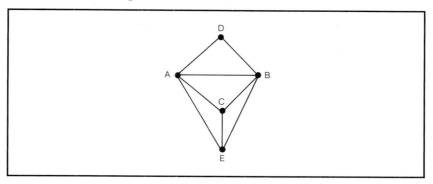

FIGURE 13-3   Roads between cities as a graph

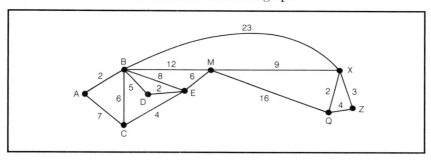

Example 13.1
Finding the Best Route between Two Nodes

A simple problem is that of finding the best route between two cities. We must define "best" in some precise way—for example, as the path with the shortest length or the path that passes through the minimum number of intermediate nodes. We will look for the route with the minimum length. The branches in a graph will be labeled with numbers that represent the distances between the nodes. One such graph is shown in Figure 13-3. Suppose we wish to find a path from node A to node Z whose length is no greater than that of any other path from A to Z.

One method of solution that should *not* be used in problems of this type is enumeration. We must not try to generate all paths between A and Z and then select the shortest: there are too many paths in a complex graph. If, for example, there are 12 cities and every city is connected to every other city by a road, there are about 40 million different paths. For 14 cities the number increases to about 6 billion paths. Because it is concerned with all possible combinations of paths, we call this a *combinatorial* problem. Enumerative methods are very poor for combinatorial problems, because the number of possibilities grows so rapidly.

Fortunately, we can eliminate many combinations. Consider Figure 13-3. Two possible paths are ABEMXZ and ACEMXZ. These paths are identical after city E. Consequently, if we find that the partial path ABE is shorter than ACE, there is no reason to consider the path starting with ACE. In fact, any path that starts with ACE can be improved by changing it to ABE. To take advantage of this observation, we will develop a method that constructs the shortest path to each intermediate city.

We can visualize a way of solving this problem as follows: suppose we have as many people as we need stationed at each city. We send one down each road leaving A, with instructions to go to the city at the end of the road and place a sign there saying how far it is from the starting point A. After the travelers arrive at the cities directly connected to A, they should similarly instruct other people to travel on to the cities directly connected to those cities. Thus, when a traveler reaches B, travelers should be sent on to cities C, D, E, M and X. When this second cadre of travelers reach their destinations, they should post signs giving the distances just traveled plus the distance of the starting city from A. In this example, the traveler leaving B and M should signpost M as being at distance 14 from A. The sign should also identify the last city along the route, saying "M is at distance 14 from A via B." In some cases, a city will already be signposted. For example, when the traveler from B to C arrives at C, there will be a sign saying that C is at distance 7 from A via A. Since the distance via B is 8, the sign should not be changed; but if the sign already posted gives a longer distance, it should be replaced. For example, if a traveler from C is the first to arrive at E, a sign showing a distance of 11 via C will be posted. When the traveler from B arrives at E, the sign will be changed to show distance 10 via B. Later, another traveler will arrive from D and post a sign showing 9 via D. Unfortunately, the earlier arrivals at E from B and C will already have sent out people to more distant cities. Therefore, this new arrival must send out additional people with the new information. Eventually, all cities connected to A will be signposted and no travelers will be arriving with shorter routes. Then all activity will stop. At this time the shortest path from any city to city A can be found by starting from that city and going back as directed by each signpost. Each city will have a pointer back to the next closest city on the best route, so the data forms a tree structure with pointers up toward the root city A, as shown in Figure 13-4. Each entry contains two data items, a city name and the distance of that city from A. In addition, each entry must have a *parental* pointer—that is, a pointer to the node above. Notice that when parental pointers are used to represent a tree structure, only one pointer need be stored in each node, even though a parent can have arbitrarily many offspring. However, only the parent of a given node can be found, and not the offspring.

FIGURE 13-4   Tree structure of best route

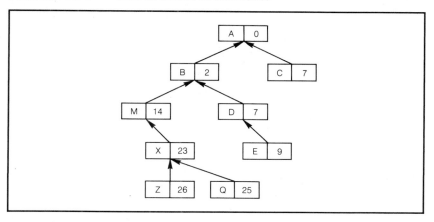

FIGURE 13-5   First part of tree

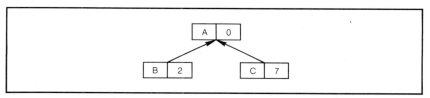

Such a tree can be constructed in a computer by simulating the behavior of our travelers. We start with the root city A and consider all roads leaving it. This enables us to construct the first part of the tree, as shown in Figure 13-5. Next we must consider all branches from the nodes we have just added. Each node connected to node B or C must be added to the tree if it is not already present. If one of these nodes is already present but the new path is shorter than the one in the tree, the node present must be removed and the new one entered. Suppose we start by considering branches from B. It is connected to A, X, M, E, D, and C. Since B is at distance 2 from the root, paths through B to these nodes will have lengths 4, 25, 14, 10, 7, and 8, respectively. Node A is the root and node C is already in the tree closer to the root than the new path, so the present entries for A and C are not changed. However, X, M, E, and D are not present, so they must be added to the tree. The result is the tree shown in Figure 13-6.

Next we must consider all branches from C. It is connected to A, B, and E. The paths from A have lengths of 14, 13, and 11, respectively. However, these paths are all longer than the existing paths in the tree, so the tree in Figure 13-6 is unchanged.

FIGURE 13-6   Expanded tree

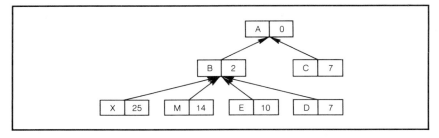

FIGURE 13-7   Tree and list of nodes to be checked

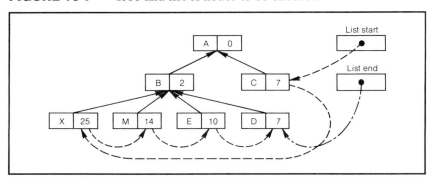

Four new nodes, X, M, E, and D, were added to the tree when branches from node B were considered. We must now consider branches from those new nodes. Let us digress for a moment and consider the problem of how we can keep a record of those nodes that have recently been added to the tree. A simple mechanism is to introduce yet another temporary data structure—specifically, a list. Whenever a new node is added to the tree, it should also be added to the end of the list if it is not already there. Initially this list is empty. When the root node A is put in the tree, it is added to the list. A node at a time can be removed from the front of the list and all roads from that node considered. Since nodes are added to the list only when a shorter path is found, no new nodes will be added after the shortest paths have been found. Therefore all nodes will eventually be removed from the list, at which time the tree will be complete. The state of the tree and list at the stage reached in Figure 13-6 is shown in Figure 13-7.

Returning to the construction of the tree, node C is now removed from the list, but its branches do not cause any new nodes to be added to the tree, and hence no new nodes are added to the list. We next remove node X from the list. It has branches to nodes Z, Q, and M. Nodes Z and Q are added to the tree and the list at distances 28 and 27, respectively. Now we remove the next node, M, from the list. It has branches to nodes Q, X, B, and E. B, E, and Q are present in the tree with shorter path lengths, so they are not changed. However, the new path to X has length 23, which is shorter than the present path to X. The existing node X in the tree is removed, and a new node X is added on a branch from M. X must also be placed in the list. This action is shown in Figure 13-8.

The nodes Z and Q that were connected to node X are no longer in the tree, so they must be discarded. This does not matter: we will reconsider branches from node X, since that node is in the list again. We also note that nodes Z and Q are still in the list. We could either remove them now or simply ignore them when we consider them later and find they are not in the tree.

Let us continue the process. Node E is removed from the list and causes no changes to the tree. Node D is removed and a shorter path of

FIGURE 13-8   Before and after adding a new node

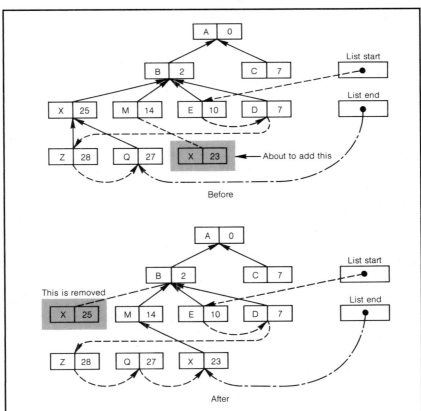

length 9 to node E is placed in the tree; E is then placed in the list again. Nodes Z and Q are removed and discarded because they are not in the tree. Next, node X is removed from the list and new paths to nodes Z and Q, of lengths 26 and 25, respectively, are added to the tree; nodes Z and Q are added to the list. Finally, nodes E, Z, and Q are removed from the list. No new paths of shorter lengths are found. The list is now empty, so the final tree is that shown in Figure 13-4. The shortest path from A to Z is via B, M, and X and has length 26.

The overall flow of the program should be studied before the details of the data structures are fixed. Program 13-1 gives an outline of the solution in terms of graph, tree, and list operations. Data declarations are omitted, because very few assumptions have been made about the actual form

■ **Program 13.1   Outline of shortest-path algorithm**

```
SHORTEST_PATH: subprogram
    mark distances of all cities as not known (e.g.,
    distance = -1)
    put starting city as root of tree and set its
    distance = 0
    put starting city in list as sole entry
    do while list not empty
```
| *Process each element added to list until the list is empty.*
| `remove city from list and call it TREE_CITY`
| `D ← distance of TREE_CITY from root city`
| `do for each city NEW_CITY directly connected`
| `to TREE_CITY`
| | *Check each road from* `TREE_CITY` *to see whether a*
| | *shorter path to a neighboring city is found.*
| | `D1 ← D + distance from TREE_CITY to`
| | `NEW_CITY`
| | `if distance of NEW_CITY from root city is`
| | `not known or is > D1`
| | | `then set distance of NEW_CITY from root`
| | | `city to D1`
| | | `set parental pointer of NEW_CITY to`
| | | `point to TREE_CITY`
| | | `put NEW_CITY in list` (*Note that it may*
| | | *already be there.*)
| | `endif`
| `enddo`
| `enddo`
```
    return
    endsubprogram SHORTEST_PATH
```

of storage. The program will have to manipulate a list, adding and removing items, to add items to a tree, to find the set of nodes in the graph directly connected to a particular node, and to find the current best distance from a city (node) to the starting city.

Before investigating ways to store the data, let us note an inefficiency in the proposed solution. It arises because many paths are explored that later turn out to be nonoptimal. Returning to the analogy with the travelers, we can see that if a traveler following a longer route arrives at a city before a traveler following a shorter route, an unnecessary set of further travelers will be dispatched with the wrong information concerning the best path. The solution in the analogy is simple—require the travelers to walk at the same speed, so that the first to arrive necessarily has the shortest path! Then it is easy to see that no path is traversed more than once in each direction. Program 13-1 can be modified to embody this idea by keeping the list of cities to be checked in ascending order of distance from the starting point. In fact, if the two list operations indicated in Program 13-1 are implemented as subprograms, no change at all is required in the main program to implement this improvement; only the two list-manipulation subprograms have to be changed.

13.1   INTERNAL REPRESENTATION OF GRAPHS

The most important consideration in determining the best way to store any data structure is the frequency with which the structure is changed relative to the frequency with which it is used. For example, if a list is stored sequentially in an array, it is easy and fast to access any element by index, but difficult to insert or delete items anywhere but at the end. If the list is not changed very often, or if it is a queue or stack that only has to be changed at the ends, then it is usually worthwhile to store it sequentially in an array. On the other hand, if the list is changed frequently other than at its ends, a chained list is preferable, because the time saved in modification offsets the extra time needed to access the elements. A graph consists of a set of nodes and, for each node, a set of branches. If the set of nodes is fixed throughout the problem, it can be stored in an array, whereas if nodes are to be inserted and deleted, a chained list should be used. Similarly, if the set of branches for each node is fixed, an array can be used; otherwise a chained list is more appropriate.

In typical applications of the shortest-path algorithm to real problems, the data in the graph is either being generated in an unknown order by another process immediately prior to the application of the shortest path algorithm or it is subject to frequent changes. (If the data is static for a long time and the shortest path algorithm is to be applied to find many paths, it is probably more efficient to precompute the shortest paths between all pairs of cities.) Therefore, for this example we will use a structure in which it is easy to modify information.

The first step in designing a storage scheme for a data structure is to determine which data items must be associated with which entries. In the shortest-path algorithm, we have to deal with nodes, branches in the graph, and a list of nodes whose branches have yet to be examined. These can be stored in a number of ways. Since we need to know the set of branches connected to each node, it is convenient to have a list of branches associated with each node. Each branch will appear twice (in the lists for the nodes at its two ends), but the ease of accessibility will improve the speed of the program.

The data associated with each type of entry is:

Nodes. DISTANCE from root, PARENT in tree, BRCHPTR to start of branch list, NAME of city

Branches. NODE at other end, LENGTH of branch

List entries. NODE to be examined, DISTANCE of node from root

(The last item is not strictly necessary, because the distance can be found by referring to the node entry.) When several data structures are to be updated in the same program, it is convenient to use the same size entry for all types of items: this allows a single free list to be used and all storage allocation to be made from the same area of memory. In this problem, one type of entry needs four data values and the others need two. In addition, all need an additional pointer to chain to the next entry of the same type, so five, three, and three values are needed, respectively. Five words could be allocated to each entry to make them of the same size, but this wastes some storage. An alternative scheme is to break the NODE entry into two entries of two and three values, respectively. The spare word in the first three-word entry can be used to point to the second. Using this technique, we adopt the scheme shown in Figure 13-9 for storing the data.

Three arrays of integers can be used to hold this information. (This as-

FIGURE 13-9   List storage for shortest-path problem

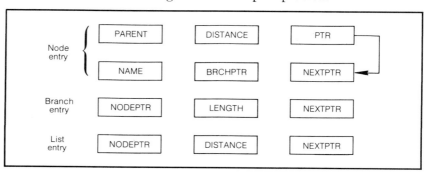

FIGURE 13-10   Simple graph and associated storage

Index	NAME PARENT NODEPTR	DISTANCE LENGTH BRCHPTR	PTR NEXTPTR	Actual entry
1	0	0	2	Node A
2	A	7	3	
3	0	−1	4	Node B
4	B	9	5	
5	0	−1	6	Node C
6	C	11	0	
7	3	3	8	Connection AB
8	5	2	0	Connection AC
9	1	3	10	Connection BA
10	5	4	0	Connection BC
11	1	2	12	Connection CA
12	3	4	0	Connection CB
13	1	0	0	List entry to node A

sumes that NAME is an integer; if it is a character string, an index to the actual name in an array of characters can be stored here.) PTR is the index of the second half of a node entry. NEXTPTR is the index of the next entry of the same type. BRCHPTR is the index of the first branch entry in a list of branches for a given node. NODEPTR is the index of the first half of a node entry. Figure 13-10 shows a simple graph and the corresponding coded entries at the start of Program 13-1. The list starts in line 13 and contains just the entry for node A. This figure illustrates the large amount of storage that chained schemes can require!

Many languages allow more than one name to be associated with a single region of storage, so that the three arrays used in the scheme above can be given multiple names. Thus NAME, PARENT, and NODEPTR can be used to name the first array, DISTANCE, LENGTH, and BRCHPTR the second, and PTR and NEXTPTR the third. This makes the program somewhat easier to read than if single names with little meaning were used for each array.

Program 13-2 is a refined version of Program 13-1 with one small change. This change allows for the possibility that an entry in the list of nodes to be checked may contain a distance larger than the current distance of the node from the root. This permits new entries to be added to the list without having to remove existing entries for the same node. If the distance given in the list entry is larger than the one currently in the node, the list entry can be ignored.

```
SHORTEST_PATH: subprogram (ROOT)
   integer ROOT,NEW_CITY,TREE_CITY,D,D1,P1
```
Compute the distance of each city from the city whose index is in
`ROOT`. *Subprogram* `INITIALIZE` *marks distance of all cities*
except `ROOT` *as* −1 *and sets the* `ROOT` *city as the root of the tree*
and the sole entry in the list starting in `LIST_START`.
```
      call INITIALIZE(ROOT)
      do while LIST_START ≠ ◻
```
      `GETLST` *gets the first entry from the list. It puts the*
      distance in `D` *and the node in* `TREE_CITY`. *(The list*
      element is returned to free storage.)
```
         call GETLST(TREE_CITY,D)
         if DISTANCE(TREE_CITY) = D
            then P1 ← BRCHPTR(PTR(TREE_CITY))
                do while P1 ≠ ◻
                   NEW_CITY ← NODEPTR(P1)
                   D1 ← D + LENGTH(P1)
                   if DISTANCE(NEW_CITY) = −1 or
                      DISTANCE(NEW_CITY) > D1
                      then DISTANCE(NEW_CITY) ←D1
                          PARENT(NEW_CITY) ←
                          TREE_CITY
```
           `PUTLST` *puts*
           `NEW_CITY` *in the list with*
           distance `D1`, *ordered by*
           increasing values of `D1`.
```
                          call PUTLST(NEW_CITY,D1)
                   endif
```
        `Advance to next connection to`
        `TREE_CITY.`
```
                   P1 ← NEXTPTR(P1)
                enddo
         endif
      enddo
      return
   endsubprogram SHORTEST_PATH
```

13.2   SPARSE MATRICES

An important example of the use of various data structures such as
graphs is the area of sparse matrices. A *sparse matrix* is a rectangular array of (usually numerical) values, a large number of which are zero or null.

In Chapter 9 we discussed the solution of linear equations. The array of coefficients, a_{ij}, of a set of linear equations is very often sparse and large. For example, the unknowns in the equations might represent the values of the air temperature at a large number of different points in the atmosphere. The equations might represent the relationships between the temperatures at neighboring points. Thus, one equation would involve only a few of the temperature unknowns, so very few of the a_{ij} would be nonzero. In typical problems of this sort, there can be as many as 1000 unknowns, but each equation may involve only about seven values. If we were to store the information using an array, only 0.7% of the array values would be nonzero. Since a 1000 by 1000 matrix has 1,000,000 elements, requiring 8 megabytes of storage if 64-bit double precision is used and the full matrix is stored, it is worth examining alternative storage techniques, called sparse storage techniques. In our example, we have to store only 7000 nonzero values, but we have to know which entries in the matrix are nonzero. There are a number of ways to do this; the best one to use depends on the application. Since we will not go into details of applications here, we will look at only a few of the storage schemes.

The simplest scheme, and one that might come to mind at first, is to store each nonzero element as its value, together with two integers giving the row and column indices of the element. If each of these integers is stored in 32 bits, a total of 128 bits is used for each nonzero; but since there are only 7000 nonzeros, the scheme uses 112 kilobytes of storage, a saving of nearly 80-fold. However, unless we are more specific about the way the elements are arranged, this scheme is not very useful.

Suppose we want to find all elements in a particular row or a particular column: How do we do it? If we want both, we need a way to find the first element in a row [column] and then move to the next element in that row [column]. This suggests storing, along with each entry, pointers to the next row and column nonzero entry. The first entries in all the rows [columns] can be found by keeping pointers to them in a pair of arrays ROW and COLUMN, each of whose ith entry is a pointer to the first nonzero in the ith row or column, respectively. This scheme stores all the information that could possibly be wanted, but adds an additional 50% storage over the previous scheme (assuming that each pointer takes 32 bits of information). However, it is still almost 50 times more concise than the full storage for the example above.

If we can modify the algorithms that use the matrices to access only rows (or only columns), we can reduce the amount of storage considerably. Suppose, for example, we only want to access rows of a sparse matrix, and that the nonzero pattern of the matrix is fixed from the start of the problem, so that we have to update only the values of the matrix, and not its structure. In that case, we can store all the rows of the matrix in contiguous locations in an array, thus saving the space of a pointer to the next element in the row. Since there is no need to access columns, we can drop the column pointer, and since all elements of a row are together, there is no need to store the row number. Thus, all we need store are the

FIGURE 13-11 Sparse matrix storage

A(I,J)

I \ J	1	2	3	4	5	6
1	15	0	0	0	22	13
2	0	19	4	0	0	0
3	-45	0	27	0	5	0
4	0	0	18	84	2	0
5	0	0	0	0	8	0
6	0	17	0	0	0	-67

	1	2	3	4	5	6	7
ROW	1	4	6	9	12	13	15

	1	2	3	4	5	6	7	8	9	10	11	12	13	14
COL	1	5	6	2	3	1	3	5	3	4	5	5	2	6
VALUE	15	22	13	19	4	-45	27	5	18	84	2	8	17	-67

entry values and their column numbers. We also need to be able to find the first entry in each row and know how long it is (how many entries). The structure shown in Figure 13-11 is a typical way of storing a sparse matrix. An array, `ROW`, contains the index of the first entry in the *I*th row in `ROW(I)`. These indices refer to a pair of arrays, `COL` and `VALUE`, containing the column number and value of each nonzero entry. Thus, since `ROW(4)` contains 9, the first entry in row 4 is in `COL(9)` and `VAL(9)`, indicating that its column number is 3 and its value is 18. The next entry in that row is in column 4 with value 84, and so on. This is found by looking at the next entry in the arrays `ROW` and `VALUE`. The total number of nonzero entries in row 4 can be found by subtracting the value of `ROW(4)` from `ROW(5)`, since we know that row 5 starts at `ROW(5)` and all spaces are used. The length of the last row is indicated by an additional (seventh) entry in the array `ROW` to indicate the first free location in the arrays `COL` and `VALUE`.

There are many other ways of storing sparse matrices, depending on the application, what algorithms are to be used, and whether only the data, or both the structure and the data, must be changed during execution.

PROBLEMS

1 Write the subprograms `INITIALIZE(ROOT)`, `GETLST(TC, D)`, and `PUTLST(NC, D)` used in Program 13-2. In addition to the arrays in global storage, you will need the start of the node list (`NODE_START`), the start of the list (`LIST_START`), and the start of the free list (`FREE_START`).

2 Write a program to print the shortest path from any node to the root of the tree, using the data structures left by Program 13-2.

3 Consider the Gauss elimination method without partial pivoting described in Chapter 9. Which of the storage schemes described for sparse matrices would be preferable? (The answer depends on whether there will be any *fill-in*, which is what occurs when an element that was previously zero becomes nonzero because of the subtraction of a multiple of another element from it. In some situations it is worthwhile first to compute which entries will fill in and then assign storage space for them. This step can be done with a knowledge of the nonzero structure of the matrix only. This can be an effective approach if several matrices with the same nonzero structure but different numerical values have to be processed.)

4 The pivot order has a large effect on the amount of fill-in (see Problem 3) in some cases. What is the best sequence of pivot elements for the matrix whose nonzero structure is indicated below? (Nonzeros are represented by x's.)

$$
\begin{array}{cccccc}
x & x & x & x & x & x \\
x & x & 0 & 0 & 0 & 0 \\
x & 0 & x & 0 & 0 & 0 \\
x & 0 & 0 & x & 0 & 0 \\
x & 0 & 0 & 0 & x & 0 \\
x & 0 & 0 & 0 & 0 & x \\
\end{array}
$$

14

Polish
Notation

■   ■   ■   ■   ■   ■   ■

In this chapter we will introduce another way of writing expressions that has the advantage that parentheses are never needed. In conventional expressions we use a hierarchy of operations in which, for example, multiplication takes precedence over addition. If we wish to write an expression in which addition is to be done before multiplication, we use parentheses, as in (A + B)*C. The purpose of the parentheses is to override the natural hierarchy of the operators. In *Polish notation* all operators have the same precedence: their position indicates the order of evaluation. This will be seen to have many benefits for the computer. People are used to writing expressions in the form used so far in this book; we are not suggesting that they should change. However, it is convenient for the computer to translate the usual form of expression into Polish form during the process of compiling a program.

Let us first consider trees as a way of representing the order in which the operations in an expression are to be executed. Note that each operation, such as multiplication, uses two operands. We have previously called these *binary* or *dyadic* operations. For the moment we will forget

FIGURE 14-1   Tree representing an arithmetic operation

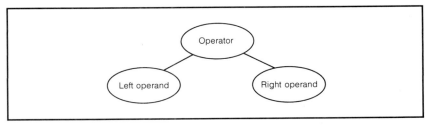

FIGURE 14-2   Tree for A − B

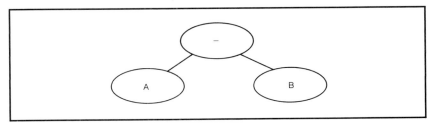

about the *unary* or *monadic* operations such as the minus in −A. We can represent each binary operation by a tree with three nodes and two branches, as shown in Figure 14-1. The root node contains the operator, and its two subnodes contain the two operands. Thus A − B would be represented as shown in Figure 14-2.

When we come to a more complex expression, such as P − Q*R, we note that the hierarchy of operators requires that the multiplication use the two operands Q and R. Thus we can construct a three-node tree for that operation. The subtraction operator uses P as its left operand and the result of the multiplication as its right operand. Thus we can construct a tree for this operation if we can find something to use for the right operand. If we think of a tree as standing for the value of the expression it represents, we can use the tree representing the multiplication operation as the right subnode of the subtraction tree. Thus P − Q*R is represented as shown in Figure 14-3. In this tree the order of the operators is determined by the fact that the multiplication must be performed first in order to provide the right operand for the subtraction: it is not dependent on any hierarchy assigned to the operators themselves. Thus if we wish to draw a tree for the expression (P − Q)*R, we can start by drawing the tree for P − Q and then use it as the left operand for the multiplication operation, as shown in Figure 14-4. That the multiplication operator has a higher precedence than the subtraction operator is irrelevant, since the structure of the tree itself indicates that the subtraction must occur first.

FIGURE 14-3   Tree for P − Q * R

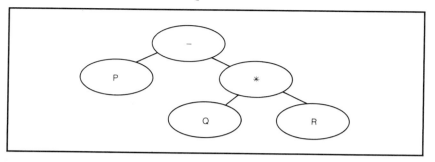

FIGURE 14-4   Tree for (P − Q) * R

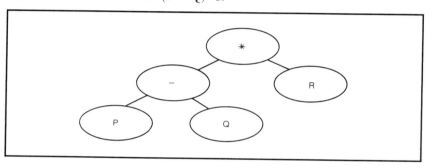

Consequently we do not need parentheses when we represent expressions as trees.

Notice that the tree representing an expression has operators in its nonterminal nodes and operands in its terminal nodes. This will always be true, since each node (except the root node) is an operand for the node above, so it either consists of data, such as P, or is a subtree that will calculate the operand. Tree structures for some more complex expressions are shown in Figure 14-5. Notice that each subtree is itself an expression, whose value is an operand for the parent node of the root of that subtree.

We can use trees to represent expressions without using parentheses and without requiring a hierarchy of operators. However, a tree is not a convenient way of storing information concisely, because, as we saw in Chapter 4, we need to store many pointers along with the information. If, however, we can find a way of writing trees in a compact form, we can use them to write expressions without parentheses. The Polish form is such a method.

Recall, from Chapter 4, that when we wanted to print a tree in order we visited each node by starting at the root node and following down to

the left until we got to a terminal node. We then printed that and came
back up to the node above and printed that, followed by the information
to the right of it. If we applied this process to the tree in Figure 14-5a, we
would print the string A*B − C + D / E. This is the original expression,
with the parentheses removed. Hence the order of the operations has
been lost. However, if we print the tree in a different order, we will find
that we can reconstruct the order of the operations. In this new order we
visit each node as before, starting at the root node, but we print the information in the node itself first, then the information to the left of it, followed by the information to the right of it. Thus we would print the tree
in Figure 14-1 as "operator," "left operand," "right operand." The tree in
Figure 14-2 would be printed as −A B. This is interpreted as "the operator subtract is to operate on the operands A and B by subtracting the second from the first." Whereas we are used to writing A − B for this opera-

FIGURE 14-5   Expressions and their trees

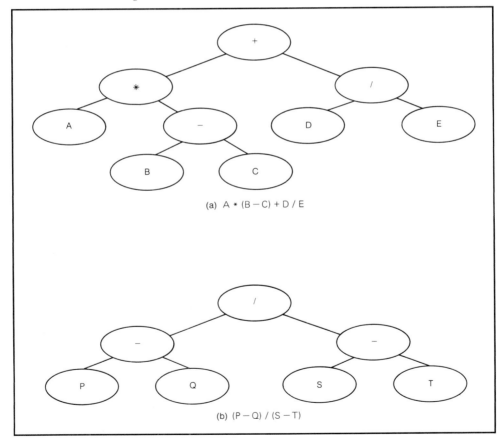

(a) A * (B − C) + D / E

(b) (P − Q) / (S − T)

tion, in the new form we write the operator first. This is called *Polish prefix* notation, because it was invented by the Polish mathematician Jan Lukasiewicz; "prefix" refers to the fact that the operator precedes the expression. (Our regular notation is called *infix* notation, because the operator is between the two operands.) If we write the tree in Figure 14-5a in prefix form, we get

+*A − B C / D E

Although this looks very strange to us, it is possible to convert it back into a unique tree and hence understand what it means.

We convert a prefix expression back into a tree by realizing that each operator has two operands. Hence if we start with the string

+ * A − B C / D E
1 2 3 4 5 6 7 8 9

(the entries have been numbered so we can refer to them in the text below), we look at the first entry (+) and then start looking for its two operands. At this time we start a tree with the plus operator as the root node. Its left subnode will be its first operand, so we look for that first. The second entry in the string is a multiplication operator. Hence it will occupy the left subnode of the root, as shown in Figure 14-6a. Since it is an operator, we temporarily abandon our search for the right subnode of the root and begin looking for two operands for the multiplication in node 2. The third element in the string is A, so this will be the left operand for node 2.* Now we can look for the right operand for node 2. The fourth entry in the string is another operator, subtraction. This becomes the right subnode of node 2, and we now start looking for two operands for it. The state of the tree at this point is shown in Figure 14-6b. The fifth and sixth entries in the string are operands, so these are the left and right subnodes of node 4. Now we have finished constructing a left operand for node 1, and we can start looking for a right operand. The seventh entry in the string is another operator, so it is the right subnode of node 1. We must look for a left and right subnode for it. We now have the tree shown in Figure 14-6c. The next two entries in the string are operands, so we finally recover the tree shown in Figure 14-5a.

Another way of understanding the meaning of a prefix expression is to draw an underline from each operator to its two operands. We can start

---

*We assume that each character in the Polish string represents an element (that is, either an operator or a piece of data). Many compilers have a "prescan" section that groups the input characters into elements called *tokens*. We will use single characters for these tokens unless they are numeric data, in which case the group of characters forming one element will be clearly delineated.

FIGURE 14-6   Stages in reconstructing a tree from a Polish prefix expression

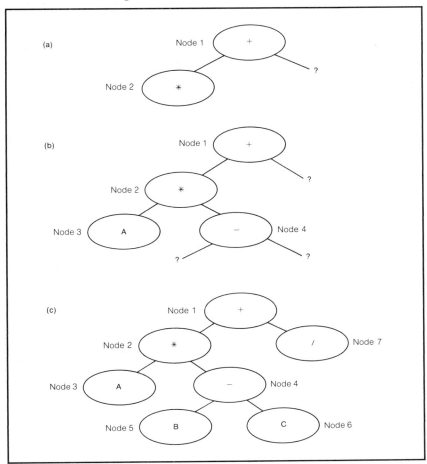

(a)

Node 1   +
?
Node 2   *

(b)

Node 1   +
?
Node 2   *
Node 3   A
−   Node 4
?   ?

(c)

Node 1   +
Node 2   *
Node 7   /
Node 3   A
−   Node 4
Node 5   B
C   Node 6

this process by working from the end of the expression and moving back to the last operator, from which a line can be drawn under the following two operands. In the example we have been using we get

+∗A − B C / D E

This means that the division operator operates on D and E. Scanning back to the left, we next come to the subtraction. A line can be drawn from it to the operands B and C to get

+∗A − B C / D E

Scanning back to the left still farther, we come to the multiplication operator. This time its first operand is A and the next is the group −B C. Thus we get

+∗A − B C / D E

Finally we scan back to the left to reach the initial addition. Its two operands are the two groups ∗A − B C and / D E. In this process we recognize a group as a single operand because we have underlined it.

This process required that we read the Polish string from the end to the beginning, but often this is inconvenient. Instead we can use *Polish postfix*, in which the operator is written *after* its two operands. Thus the infix expression A − B would be written A B − in postfix notation. This corresponds to reading through the tree in the same order as before, but writing the left and right operands before the operator. Using the same example (Figure 14-5a), we start at the root node containing the addition operator. First we must write the left operand, so we follow down to the left and come to the multiplication. Before we can write it, we must write its two operands. The left is A, so it can be written immediately. The right is a subtree starting at the subtraction, so its operands must be written first: they are B and C. Now we come back to the subtraction node: since both its operands are now written, we can write down the subtraction operator itself. So far we have the string A B C −. We back up to the multiplication node and can now write it down. This brings us back to the root node containing the addition, but we still have to write down its right operand. This results in the three entries D E /; then we can finally write down the addition to get:

A B C − ∗D E / +

If we wish to reconstruct the tree from postfix form, it is easier to start from the right-hand end, where the root appears. However, we can read from left to right to find out which are the operands for the various operators. We read to the first operator and draw a line back to the previous two operands. This results in

A B C − ∗D E / +

telling us that the subtraction operates on B and C. Now we draw a line back from the multiplication. Its operands are A and the group already underlined. This gives

A B C −∗D E / +

The scan continues and we come to the division. Its operands are D and E, so we underline those to get

A B C −*D E / +

Finally we come to the plus sign, and find that its operands are the two groups A B C −* and D E /.

We have not mentioned unary operators, such as the minus sign in D*(− D + E). In fact, there are three different uses of the symbol − in an expression. In A − B*(− C + −3.5), the first − symbol is the familiar binary subtraction operator. The second is the unary minus sign, meaning that we are to use the negative of the value of C. The third is part of the number-naming process: that is, the string −3.5 names a certain number that is to be used as an operand in the addition operation. This use is not as an operator at all. In normal use we write the same symbol for all three cases.

We cannot use one symbol for several purposes in Polish notation. If we see the symbol − as an entry in a string, for example, we will look for its two operands. Therefore, we must use a different symbol for the unary minus. Let us use the lowercase letter m. The tree corresponding to A − B*(− C + −3.5) is shown in Figure 14-7. The binary subtraction in node 1 has two subnodes, whereas the unary minus in node 6 has only one subnode. The prefix and postfix forms for this tree are

−A*B + m C −3.5

FIGURE 14-7   Tree for A − B * (− C + − 3.5)

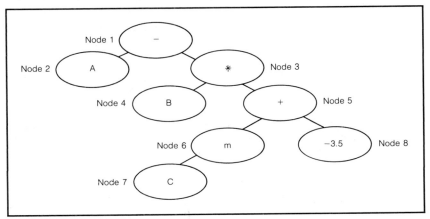

and

A B C m −⊐.5 + * −

respectively. Notice that the group −⊐.5 is a single entry in the Polish string.

As before, we can convert the forms back into their tree representations or we can understand them by underlining the groups. We get

+A*B + m C −⊐.5

and

A B C m −⊐.5 + *−

respectively, for the prefix and postfix forms of the example above.

When Polish strings are stored inside a computer, they will be encoded in such a way that each entry is separated from the next. For example, operators will probably be represented by integers, possibly 1 for +, 2 for −, 3 for *, and so forth; data will probably be represented by the addresses of table entries describing that data (for example, the name of the variable, whether it is an integer or a real, etc.).

14.1 EVALUATING POLISH EXPRESSIONS

An important advantage of Polish postfix expressions is that it is a simple matter for a computer program to evaluate them. In this section we will study the automatic evaluation of expressions, represented first as trees and then as Polish postfix expressions. In the following section we will examine a method for converting the usual infix expressions into Polish postfix form.

Suppose we wish to find the value of the tree shown in Figure 14-8a. It is evident that we must start by executing an operator that has terminal nodes for both operands. One way we can find such an operator is to read the tree in the usual left-to-right fashion, starting from the root. We should read each node containing an operator in the order "left subnode, right subnode, operation." If a subnode in turn contains an operator, it must be read in the same fashion before the reading of its parent can continue. Eventually we will come to an element with both subnodes terminal—that is, containing data. In Figure 14-8a this is the division in node 4, which will be read in the order "left subnode (3.6), right subnode (2),

FIGURE 14-8   Evaluating a tree expression

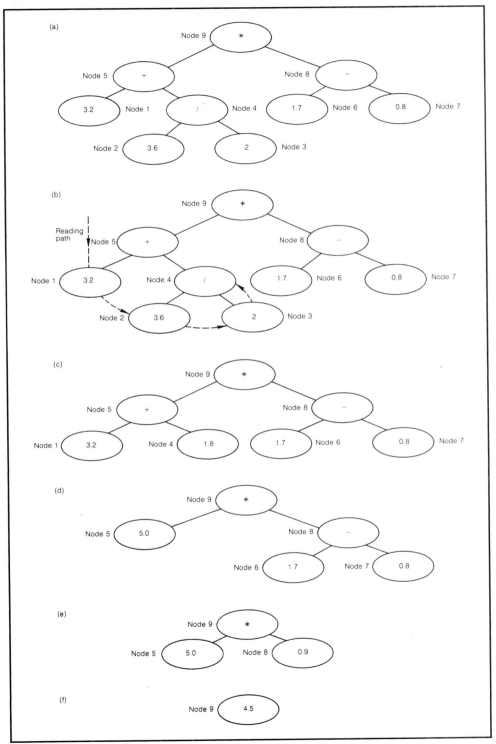

divide." The reading path is shown by the dashed lines in Figure 14-8b. At the time we first read an operator, the last two items read were its operands. Therefore we can apply the division operator to the operands 3.6 and 2 to get the result 1.8. The subtree rooted on the division operator can then be replaced by a terminal node containing 1.8. We have removed one operator and simplified the tree.

An identical process can now be applied to this simplified tree. Again we will find that the first time we complete the reading of a node in the form "left subnode, right subnode, operator," we will just have read the two operands for the operator. The successive stages of such an evaluation are shown in Figures 14-8c to 14-8f.

The mechanism just proposed for evaluating a tree expression requires that the expression be scanned repeatedly from left to right to look for an operator "at the bottom" of the tree. The rescanning is not necessary if we keep track of the path we have already followed in reading the tree. Look back at Figure 14-8c and notice the path that has been followed in reading the tree. Now notice that after the division has been performed, the two nodes read prior to the division have been removed, and the result of the division (1.8) has replaced the division operator in its node. If we draw what remains of the reading path of the tree in Figure 14-8c, we get the path shown in Figure 14-9a. If we continue reading we will come back up to the addition operator, as shown in Figure 14-9b. This path is exactly the one that would be followed if we started reading the reduced tree from the beginning. Now the preceding two nodes on the reading path are the operands for the addition. If we perform this operation, the tree and the reading path are collapsed, as shown in Figure 14-9c.

The reading path consists of a list of nodes that have already been read. It will contain only data in all places except possibly the last. Even there, the presence of an operator is temporary, because it is immediately executed, using the two preceding entries on the list as operands. Since we work only on the end of the list, it is in fact being used as a *stack* (see Chapter 3). Instead of building a list of nodes that have been read, we could put their contents into a stack. In the example of Figure 14-8b, the state of the stack after the first three nodes on the reading path have been read would be as in Figure 14-10a. When the next node (containing the division) is read, the last two entries on top of the stack are combined by dividing the lower by the upper. The result is put back in the stack, as shown in Figure 14-10b. The next node to be read contains the addition operation. It is immediately executed on the top two entries of the stack to get the result shown in Figure 14-10c. Successive states of the stack before and after reading each of the remaining operators are shown in the remainder of Figure 14-10. The final state of the stack is a single entry containing the value of the original expression.

At this point we note that the order in which we have been reading the tree is precisely that of a Polish postfix expression: the two operands are read, followed by the operator. Thus if we are given such an expression,

FIGURE 14-9   Reduction of reading paths

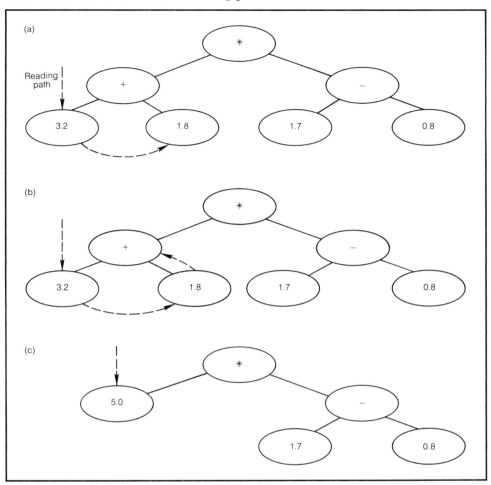

FIGURE 14-10   States of a stack

	Before divide	After divide	After add	Before subtract	After subtract	After multiply
	2			0.8		
	3.6	1.8		1.7	0.9	
	3.2	3.2	5.0	5.0	5.0	4.5
	(a)	(b)	(c)	(d)	(e)	(f)

FIGURE 14-11   Evaluation of a postfix string

Expression remaining to be read	Stack (top →)		
31.5,2,3.5,*,m,/,3,1.5,/,+			
2,3.5,*,m,/,3,1.5,/,+	31.5		
3.5,*,m,/,3,1.5,/,+	31.5	2	
*,m,/,3,1.5,/,+	31.5	2	3.5
m,/,3,1.5,/,+	31.5	7	
/,3,1.5,/,+	31.5	−7	
3,1.5,/,+	−4.5		
1.5,/,+	−4.5	3	
/,+	−4.5	3	1.5
+	−4.5	2	
	−2.5		

we now know how to evaluate it using a stack. Whenever an operand is read, it is placed in the stack. When an operator is read it is executed, using the top entries in the stack as data and returning the result to the top of the stack. The evaluation of $31.5 / - (2*3.5) + 3 / 1.5$, represented by the postfix expression $31.5,2,3.5,*,m,/,3,1.5,/,+$, is shown in Figure 14-11. The operation m is unary minus; the items in the expression have been separated by commas for clarity. Notice that the unary minus is executed between the fifth and sixth lines of Figure 14-11. Since it is a monadic operator requiring only one operand, it uses only the top item in the stack and returns the result to the same place.

PROBLEMS

1 Convert the following infix expressions into trees and into postfix and prefix expressions:
a. A + B*C / D
b. −A − C*D + B ↑ E
c. (P + Q / R) / (S − T)
d. X ↑ Y ↑ (−Z)

2 Convert the following prefix expressions into trees and into infix and postfix expressions:
a. +*− A B C D
b. + m A*B m C
c. ↑ + P / Q R − S T
d. ↑ X*Y Z W

3 Convert the following trees into prefix, postfix, and infix expressions:

a.

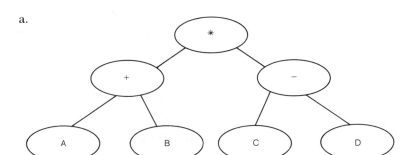

b.

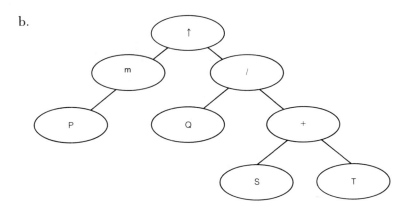

4 What is the value of the following postfix expressions?
  a. 5.1 3 m +
  b. 4.8 m 1.3 2 * −
  c. 1.2 1.3 + 1.4 1.1 + *
  d. 2 4.5 1.5 / 2 * 6 + −

5 Write a program to input and convert a prefix expression into a tree. (Note that a binary tree can be used, so storage of the tree structure can be simple.) For the program, you can assume any suitably simple form of input coding. For example, positive integers can be used for operands and negative integers for operators.

6 Write a program to convert the tree structure from Problem 5 into postfix form and to print it in that form.

7 Assume that a postfix expression is stored in the array K in the following way. Each item occupies one location. If an item is an operation, it is a negative integer with one of the following values:

$$
\begin{array}{cc}
+ & -1 \\
- & -2 \\
* & -3 \\
/ & -4 \\
\uparrow & -5 \\
m & -6 \\
\end{array}
$$

If an item is an operand, it is a positive integer J such that the value of the data is in A(J). Write a program to evaluate postfix expressions. Assume that the postfix string is terminated by the integer 0.

C H A P T E R

15

Syntax Analysis and Conversion to Postfix

■ ■ ■ ■ ■ ■ ■

The *syntax* of a language is the structure of that language, and *syntax analysis* is the determination of the structure of a statement in that language. Thus, if the language is English, a syntax analysis of the statement

The boy hits the ball.

is used to determine that boy and ball are nouns, the first being the subject of the sentence and the second the object. Syntax analysis can then be used to see that

\<subject\> \<verb\> \<object\>

is a valid sentence. If the language is a programming language, a syntax analysis is used to determine the structure of a string such as A ← B + C. We first determine that B and C are operands, then see that B + C is an expression that is a valid right-hand side and that A is a valid left-hand side, and finally determine that

$$\text{<left-hand side>} \leftarrow \text{<right-hand side>}$$

is a valid assignment statement.

In this chapter we will study the problem of converting an infix expression into its equivalent postfix form. To do this we have to determine the syntax of the expression. If there are syntax errors, as in the expression B*/C, we cannot find a meaningful structure. In this case a compiler analyzing the expression should not come to an abrupt termination, but should localize the error as much as possible before continuing to scan the input for other errors.

The basic operation in converting infix to postfix is that of moving the operator from its position between the two operands to a position following them. Thus A + B becomes A B +. Hence if we are presented with a string A + B and we read it from left to right, we must save the addition operator when we read it until after we have read its second operand. However, we can write out the operands immediately as we read them. Now let us consider the infix string

A + B ↑ C*D / E

How do we determine that the operands for the multiplication are B ↑ C and D? We must use the hierarchy of the operators shown in Table 15-1. In this table, the operators with "higher" hierarchy are performed before those with lower hierarchy. Those of equal hierarchy are done from left to right.

We now return to our example,

A + B ↑ C*D / E

TABLE 15-1 Hierarchy of Operators

Operator	Meaning	Hierarchy
Unary + or −	Unary + or −	Highest
↑	Exponentiation	2nd highest
* or /	Multiplication or division	3rd highest
+ or −	Addition or subtraction	4th highest
←	Assignment	Lowest

TABLE 15-2 Conversion of Infix to Postfix

Input String (Infix)	Output String (Postfix)	Stack (Top→)	Precedence Comparison
A + B ↑ C*D/E△			
+ B ↑ C*D/E△	A		
B ↑ C*D/E△	A	+	
↑ C*D/E△	A B	+	
C*D/E△	A B	+ ↑	↑ > +
*D/E△	A B C	+ ↑	
*D/E△	A B C ↑	+	* < ↑
D/E△	A B C ↑	+ *	* > +
/E△	A B C ↑ D	+ *	
/E△	A B C ↑ D*	+	/ = *
E△	A B C ↑ D*	+ /	/ > +
△	A B C ↑ D*E	+ /	
△	A B C ↑ D*E /	+	△ < /
△	A B C ↑ D*E / +		△ < +

Exponentiation has a higher precedence than multiplication, so the variable C, which is immediately to the left of the multiplication, is an operand for the exponentiation rather than for the multiplication. B ↑ C is an operand in turn for either the addition on its left or the multiplication on its right. Since addition has a lower precedence than multiplication, B ↑ C is an operand for the multiplication. Similarly we look to the right of the multiplication for its second operand. Division has the same precedence as multiplication. Since our rule for operators having equal precedence is that the left operator is evaluated first, D is an operand for the multiplication. Using this approach, we can convert the expression by reading it from left to right. The process will be described below and is illustrated in Table 15-2.

First we read the variable A and output it into the postfix string. Then we read the addition operator. The preceding operand must be the first operand for the addition. However, we must save the addition until we have found its second operand and have output this operand into the post-fix string. We continue reading and output the next operand B into the postfix string. Next we read the exponentiation operator. Since exponentiation has a higher precedence than the saved addition, the last variable output (B) is the first operand for the exponentiation. Therefore we must also save the exponentiation until we have found its second operand. Next we read C and output it to the postfix string. Then we read the multiplication operator, which has a lower precedence than the exponentiation that was saved most recently. Therefore the variable just output (C) is the second operand for the exponentiation, so this operator can be output. So far our postfix string has the form

A B C ↑

Before we encountered the exponentiation, we were trying to find the second operand for the addition, so we return to looking for that operand. We have just read the multiplication operator and done nothing with it, so we must now compare it with the addition we have been saving. Since multiplication has a higher precedence than addition, the compound operand B ↑ C just processed must be the left operand for the multiplication rather than the right operand for the addition. Therefore we save the multiplication until we have found its right operand. As we continue reading the input string, we read and output the next variable D and come to the division operation. Since this has the same priority as multiplication, the last variable read (D) is the right operand of the multiplication, so the multiplication can be put into the output string to get

A B C ↑ D*

Now we are back to looking for the rest of the second operand of the addition. Since the division just read has higher precedence than the addition, it is saved. We read and output the operand E and then come to the end of the expression. This is signaled by a special mark, or is indicated by a count of the number of items in the string. In Table 15-2 it is indicated by the symbol Δ. We can view the end of the expression as an operator of lowest precedence. Hence we can now output the division just saved, which has operands B*C ↑ D and E. This leaves only the addition to be processed. Since it also has higher precedence than the end of the expression, we have finally found its second operand, and we can output it to get

A B C ↑ D*E / +

During this process it was necessary to save various operators until their second operands had been processed. When a new operator had to be saved, we temporarily ignored the earlier ones until we had processed the most recent. Thus we should save these operators on a stack. Each new one to be saved is placed in the stack; we concern ourselves with only the operator on top of the stack.

The process just described handles any valid combination of binary operators and operands. However, it does not allow for parentheses or for unary operators. Parentheses can be handled easily once we understand how they fit into the hierarchy. Their purpose is to override the natural hierarchy, in which multiplication takes precedence over addition and so forth. Any subexpression enclosed within parentheses must be evaluated immediately: it then takes the place of an operand for an operator outside the parentheses. Thus if we have the expression A*(B + C − D) / E, we must realize that the parentheses enclosing the addition and subtraction operators give them a higher precedence than the multiplication and division operators. If we start processing this expression by the algorithm given above, we will first output the operand A, then put the multiplication operator into the stack. The process is illustrated in Table 15-3. If we ignore the left parenthesis, we will output the operand B and then come to the addition operator. Somehow we must recognize that this has a higher precedence than the multiplication operator currently in the stack. We could do this if we had put a mark on top of the stack to show that a parenthesis had been read. In fact, this mark could be the parenthesis itself if we had not ignored it but had put it in the stack. Thus our rule is that *a parenthesis on top of the stack has a lower precedence than any other operator read from the input.*

However, when we first read the left parenthesis, we put it in the stack. Therefore, our rule must also provide that *a left parenthesis in the input*

TABLE 15-3 Handling Parentheses

Input String (Infix)	Output String (Postfix)	Stack (Top →)	Comments
A*(B + C − D)/EΔ			
*(B + C − D)/EΔ	A		
(B + C − D)/EΔ	A	*	
B + C − D)/EΔ	A	*(	(higher than *
+ C − D)/EΔ	A B	*(	
C − D)/EΔ	A B	*(+	+ higher than (
− D)/EΔ	A B C	*(+	
− D)/EΔ	A B C +	*(	+ = −
D)/EΔ	A B C +	*(−	− higher than
)/EΔ	A B C + D	*(−	(
)/EΔ	A B C + D −	*(	
/EΔ	A B C + D −	*	) lower than −
			Matching
			parentheses
/EΔ	A B C + D −*		discarded
EΔ	A B C + D −*	/	/ = *
Δ	A B C + D −*E	/	
Δ	A B C + D −*E /		
			Δ lower than /

string *has a higher precedence than anything in the stack* and should be put into the stack like an operator.

If we follow this process, we will continue scanning the expression A∗(B + C − D) / E and output the variables A, B, and C, by which time the stack will contain ∗, (, and +. When the subtraction is encountered, the addition on top of the stack is output, since it has the same priority as subtraction. Then the subtraction is put into the stack, since it is higher than the left parenthesis in the stack, and the variable D is output. Now we reach the right parenthesis in the input that closes up the parenthesized expression. This means that the subtraction in the stack must be output, since the last operand read (D) is its second operand. Now we are in a state in which the stack has a left parenthesis on top and the last entry read from the input string is a right parenthesis. Since the left parenthesis was saved while we were processing the part of the string within the parentheses, we must have finished processing this part of the string, and the output postfix string must now contain a translated form of that subexpression. Consequently we can discard the parenthesis on top of the stack and continue scanning the input string. Next we read the division operator. Its precedence is equal to that of the multiplication on top of the stack, so we output the multiplication operator followed by the variable E, and the division operator is placed in the stack. Finally the end-of-expression character Δ (which has the lowest precedence of all) is encountered, causing the division to be removed from the stack and output, and the process to terminate.

Program 15-1 converts an input string of tokens representing an infix expression *without* parentheses into a Polish postfix expression. Syntax errors are detected when the string does not consist of alternating operands and operators. Initially, the special marker Δ is pushed into the stack. It is assumed to have lower precedence than any operator and to match the precedence of the Δ marker at the end of the string. It will

■ **Program 15.1   Translating infix to postfix—no parentheses**

POSTFIX: **program**
   The input is read, a token at a time. The output is a Polish postfix
   expression. Data types of tokens are not declared, although
   typically they would be represented as integers.
   logical OPERAND_EXPECTED, NEXT_INPUT_
   PROCESSED
      initialize stack to empty
      push △ into stack
      The △ is pushed into the stack as a bottom marker. It will
      match the end-of-string indicator, and should be given the
      same precedence.

```
        OPERAND_EXPECTED ← true
        NEXT_INPUT_PROCESSED ← true
        do while stack not empty
            if NEXT_INPUT_PROCESSED
            then input NEXT_INPUT
            endif
            NEXT_INPUT_PROCESSED ← false
            if OPERAND_EXPECTED
                then
                    if NEXT_INPUT is an operand
                        then
                            output NEXT_INPUT to Polish
                            string
                            OPERAND_EXPECTED ← false
                            NEXT_INPUT_PROCESSED ←
                            true
                        else
                            output 'SYNTAX ERROR'
                            NEXT_INPUT_PROCESSED ←
                            true
                        endif
                else
                    if NEXT_INPUT is an operator
                        then
                            case precedence of
                            NEXT_INPUT is (lower, equal,
                            higher) than precedence of
                            top of stack
                                lower: pop stack and
                                output to Polish string
                                equal: pop stack and
                                output to Polish string
                                higher: push NEXT_INPUT
                                into stack
                                NEXT_INPUT_PROCESSED←
                                true
                                OPERAND_EXPECTED ← true
                            endcase
                        else
                            output 'SYNTAX ERROR'
                            NEXT_INPUT_PROCESSED ←
                            true
                        endif
                endif
        enddo
endprogram POSTFIX
```

be output to the Polish postfix expression when the translation has been completed. The logical variable OPERAND_EXPECTED indicates whether the next input token is expected to be an operand or operation.

Program 15-1 can be modified to handle parentheses by changing the first **else** clause to

```
else
    if NEXT_INPUT = '('
        then push NEXT_INPUT into stack
        else output 'SYNTAX ERROR'
        endif
    NEXT_INPUT_PROCESSED ← true
```

and the cases in the case statement to

```
lower:
    if top of stack = '('
        then
            output 'SYNTAX ERROR, TOO MANY LEFT
            PARENTHESES'
            pop stack
        else
            pop stack and output to Polish string
        endif
equal:
    if top of stack = '('
        then
            pop stack
            NEXT_INPUT_PROCESSED ← true
        else
            pop stack and output to Polish string
        endif
higher:
    if NEXT_INPUT = ')'
        then
            output 'SYNTAX ERROR, TOO MANY RIGHT
            PARENTHESES'
        else
            push NEXT_INPUT into stack
            OPERAND_EXPECTED ← true
        endif
    NEXT_INPUT_PROCESSED ← true
```

When an operand is expected and a left parenthesis is read, it is pushed into the stack and another operand sought. When a right parenthesis is read as an operator, it has the same precedence as a left parenthesis in the stack, a higher precedence than the bottom-of-stack marker Δ, and a lower precedence than anything else in the stack. This allows us to detect the cases when the next input and top of stack are one of the three pairs [Δ, (], [), Δ], and [), (]. The first two are syntax errors; the third is valid, and causes the input and top of stack to be discarded.

PROBLEMS

1 How would you include the operators **and**, **or**, and **not** in Table 15-1?

2 Describe the changes necessary in Program 15-1 to handle the unary minus operator.

16

The Critical-
Path Method

■   ■   ■   ■   ■   ■   ■

The critical-path method, or CPM, is an important tool in many industrial applications. It is used to predict the length of time a project will take and what will be the critical tasks whose delay would delay the whole project. It is a good example of the application of graphs to real problems.

Imagine a construction contractor planning to build a large structure. The job involves many subcontractors and groups of workers performing different tasks, such as digging the hole for the foundations, pouring the concrete into the foundations, erecting the steel frame, pouring the concrete floors, putting in the plumbing and electrical wiring, painting, landscaping, and so forth. In a large construction job there may be thousands of such tasks.

The client who ordered the building will want to know how long it will take to finish it. The contractor will want to know when to bring in groups for particular tasks. If, for example, the electricians are brought in before enough of the shell is finished, they will be unable to work and time will be wasted, increasing the cost of the building. If they are brought in too late, completion may be delayed, causing other, hidden costs. The contractor might therefore construct a list of all the necessary tasks and indi-

TABLE 16-1 Task Completion Schedule

Task	Task Description	Completion Time (weeks)	Other Tasks That Must Be Finished First
1	Clear site	2	
2	Dig hole	3	1
3	Pour foundations	2	2
4	Erect steel frame	3	3
5	Install drains	2	3
6	Install plumbing	4	4, 5
.	.	.	.
.	.	.	.
.	.	.	.
1021	Paint	5	1020, 1003, 1007
1022	Landscape	4	1019, 1011
1023	Hand over to client	0	1000, 1021, 1022

FIGURE 16-1 Graph of Table 16-1

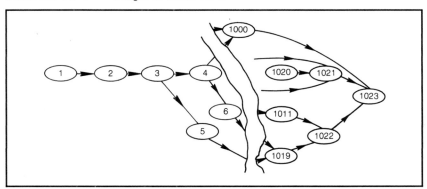

cate which tasks must be finished before each task can be started. An estimate of how long each task will take to complete should also be made. This might lead to a table like Table 16-1 for a particular job.

This mass of information can be represented by a directed graph. Suppose we use nodes to represent the starts of various tasks. Thus node 1 represents the start of site clearance, node 6 the start of plumbing installation, and so forth. A directed branch should be drawn in the graph from node X to node Y if node X must be finished before node Y can be started. Thus Table 16-1 becomes the graph shown in Figure 16-1.

Chapter 16, The Critical-Path Method   **185**

This graph is a *partially ordered* set of nodes, in that each pair of nodes may be unrelated (as are nodes 4 and 5) or may satisfy one of these relations: node X occurs before node Y, or Y occurs before node X. We will write these relations as X < Y or Y < X, respectively. Furthermore, it can never happen that X < Y, Y < Z, and Z < X, because this would be equivalent to saying that job X must be finished before job Y, which must be finished before job Z, which must be finished before job X. It would be difficult to start any of these jobs. Formally, such a graph is called a *directed acyclic graph*, or DAG for short.

To shorten the discussion below, we will talk about "completing a node," meaning "completing the task represented by that node." We can assign a time to each node: the earliest time when it can be finished. We can find this by arbitrarily calling the start of work time 0 and labeling those nodes with no input branches (node 1 in our example) as being finished in their stated completion times. Thus node 1 could be finished in two weeks, so it would be assigned a completion time of 2. We can then assign completion time 5 to node 2, 7 to node 3, 10 to node 4, and 9 to node 5. Node 6 cannot be started until both nodes 4 and 5 have been finished, so it cannot start until time 10. It can therefore be finished at time 14. The start of the graph for Table 16-1 is shown in Figure 16-2. The nodes contain their node numbers, followed by completion times in parentheses.

In this way we can proceed through the whole graph. When all the nodes preceding a given node have been assigned completion times, that node can be processed. Its completion time is the maximum of the completion times of all the preceding nodes plus the time required to perform the task represented by the node itself.

In Figure 16-2 we see that node 6 cannot be started until nodes 4 and 5 have been completed; however, node 4 will not be completed until a week later than node 5. If there are no delays, node 4 is the critical factor that determines when node 6 can start. Therefore, if our concern is to complete node 6 as quickly as possible, we must be concerned with completing node 4, node 3, node 2, and node 1. We say that for the subgraph consisting of nodes 1 through 6 only, the path through nodes 1, 2, 3, 4,

FIGURE 16-2   Start of the graph of Table 16-1

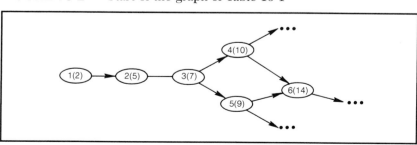

FIGURE 16-3   Critical path

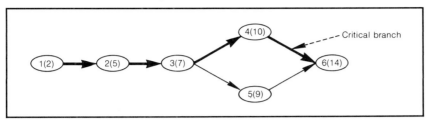

FIGURE 16-4   Indicating completion line on branches

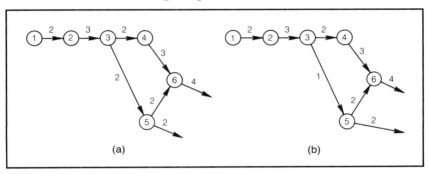

and 6 is *critical*, because a delay of any node on this path will delay the completion of the final node. The critical path is shown as a thick line in Figure 16-3. Formally, a critical path is the set of nodes and branches whose least delay will delay the completion of the last node in the graph.

In the representation above we associated task times with nodes; we will now change the description a little by associating the task times with the branches leaving a node. Thus the start of Figure 16-1 would be redrawn as in Figure 16-4a. The numbers on the branches are the times from the start of the task in the node on the left to the time that the node on the right can be started. This allows the graph to represent the fact that some tasks can be started when other tasks have progressed only part-way. Thus in Table 16-1 it could be that the foundations (task 3) are actually poured in one week, at which time the drains can be installed (task 5), but that they must be allowed to harden another week before the steel frame can be erected on them (task 4). To show this we can indicate that the branch from node 3 to node 4 requires two weeks and the branch from node 3 to node 5 only one week. Then the graph would start as in Figure 16-4b.

In a job involving many tasks, the identification of the critical path, although a trivial computational process, makes it possible for a contractor to decide which tasks should be given high priority when allotting labor and other facilities. It also allows the identification of tasks that can be delayed without delaying the whole job and times when the completion schedule is likely to change because of delays.

It is evident that a building contractor will not write a program to handle this problem for each new building. In fact, apart from a few very large construction companies, contractors seldom have programming expertise. However, critical-path problems are common in all large construction jobs, from buildings to submarines to large electronic products (such as computers). Therefore, a number of standard programs have been written for CPM—also called PERT (progress evaluation in real time). A user prepares the data in a form dictated by the program and the computer system to be used, and uses one of these standard programs. The data and the standard program are submitted to the computer and the answers are returned—in this case, a list of the critical paths in the job.

16.1 FINDING CRITICAL PATHS

How can we go about finding a critical path? First, it is convenient to put the graph into a standard form with only one starting node and only one finishing node. This can be done as follows: add one more node and make it a predecessor to each node with no other predecessors. It can be called "Start the Job." Branches from this node take zero time. Then add a terminal node—that is, one that has no successors—which is a successor to all nodes that were previously terminal.

With these changes we can now give rules for finding the critical path and hence for finding the length of time to completion. The process described assigns a minimum starting time to each node. This time is the earliest point at which the task represented by the node can be started. First we set the starting time of the "Start the Job" node to zero. Then each node Z in the graph that has starting times for all of its predecessor nodes is assigned a starting time by examining each branch coming into it. For each branch, the sum of the branch time and the starting time of the node the branch comes from is computed. The maximum for all incoming branches is identified and assigned as the minimum starting time for node Z. This is illustrated in Figure 16-5. The predecessors of node 6 are 2, 3, and 5. Since the starting times of these nodes are 1, 2, and 3, respectively, and the branch times before task 6 can start are 6, 5, and 2, respectively, we compute the maximum of $1 + 6$, $2 + 5$, and $3 + 2$. This is 7, so node 6 is assigned the minimum starting time of 7.

We can work from left to right with this rule until we have assigned starting times to all the nodes in the graph. The last node in the graph is the extra node we added, so its starting time will be the minimum completion time for the whole job. We can now work backward from this node to find the critical path. Each branch into the terminal node must be checked. If the starting time of the node the branch comes from plus the

FIGURE 16-5 Minimum starting times

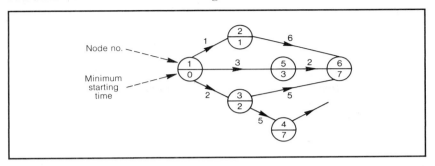

FIGURE 16-6 Critical paths and critical nodes

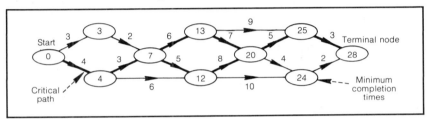

branch time is equal to the starting time of the terminal node, the branch is marked as a critical branch and the node it comes from is marked as a critical node. Now each critical node is treated in the same way. This may result in one or more branches and nodes being marked critical. Eventually all critical nodes and branches—in particular, the starting node—will be marked. The critical path is the collection of branches marked as critical. An example is shown in Figure 16-6. The thick branches are critical.

Before writing a program for this process, let us restate an outline of the algorithm. Initially, no nodes are marked with start times. Let us denote the fact that the start time for a node is not known by saying that it is in set U. (U stands for *unknown.*) Initially, the starting node is assigned a start time of zero, so it can be removed from set U. We will say that it is now in set S. The first stage of the algorithm entails searching set U to find an element whose input branches are all connected to elements in set S. When one is found, it can be moved to set S after its minimum starting time is calculated. The idea of searching through a potentially large set is not appealing: we may have to search the whole set to find each node to remove from U to S. So before we continue to the second stage, let us change the algorithm a little. When we move an element from set U to set S, we can check to see whether the move has made it possible to calculate the starting times for any of the nodes on the ends of the output branches from that element. These nodes can be placed in a new set, U1. Then, instead of searching through U for an element to move to S, we can take any element from U1. When U1 is empty, the first stage is complete. At this time, set U should be empty. If it is not, the graph is not acyclic: there is a loop present. It does not represent a feasible job.

In the second stage of the algorithm, we must identify the critical nodes and branches. Call the set of critical nodes set C. We start by placing the terminal node in set C. Now we search set C to see which nodes at the ends of input branches to elements in set C are also critical. Such nodes must be moved from set S to set C. The process is completed when no more nodes can be moved from set S to set C. Again, we should try to avoid a long search. This can be done by using another set, set C1, of nodes that have been found to be critical but whose input branches have not yet been examined. Initially, the terminal node is placed in set C1. As long as C1 is not empty, a node is removed from it and the input branches of that node examined. If any of the branches are critical, the nodes at the other end are placed in set C1. As nodes are removed from set C1 they are placed in set C. The process is complete when set C1 is empty. At that time, set C contains all the critical nodes, and the critical branches are those between pairs of critical nodes. (These branches could also have been marked during the second phase of the process.) Program 16-1 gives this outline more formally. The variable declarations are not shown in Program 16-1, since it is only an outline. The first part describes the over-all program; Programs 16-1a and 16-1b are further refinements of two of the lines in 16-1. Since they are intended to replace those lines, they have been called code segments.

■ **Program 16.1   Critical-path method**

```
CPM: program
    Determine the set C of critical nodes of an acyclic graph.
    ST(NODE) is the start time of a node. TIME(BRANCH) is the
    time it takes to complete the work represented by a branch.
        place all nodes in set U ("Unknown")
        move initial node to set U1 (Nodes whose minimum
        start time is known but whose successors have not yet been
        checked.)
        ST(INITIAL_NODE) ← 0
        determine start time of all nodes and put them
        in set S (See Program 16-1a.)
        if set U not empty
            then
                output 'INVALID DATA,LOOP DETECTED'
            else
                move terminal node to set C1 (Nodes that are
```

> *critical but whose predecessors have not yet been checked.)*
>> determine all critical nodes and put them in set C *(See Program 16-1b.)*
> endif
> return
> endprogram CPM

■ **Program 16.1a   Code segment to assign start times**

determine start time of all nodes and put them in set S: codesegment

> *Move nodes from set U1 to S. As each is moved, check all successors to see whether their start times can be computed. If so, put them in set U1.*

```
do while set U1 not empty
    NODE ← any element of U1
    move NODE to set S
    do for each BRANCH into NODE
        T ← max of TIME(BRANCH) + ST(node at
        other end of BRANCH)
        enddo
    ST(NODE) ← T
    do for each BRANCH out of NODE
        if start time can be computed for node
        at other end of BRANCH
            then put node at other end of BRANCH
            in set U1
            endif
        enddo
    enddo
endcodesegment
```

■ **Program 16.1b   Code segment to find critical nodes**

determine all critical nodes and put them in set C: codesegment

> *Move nodes from set C1 to set C. As each is moved, check all predecessors to determine which ones are critical, and place those in set C1.*

```
do while set C1 not empty
    Node ← any element of C1
    move NODE to set C
    do for each BRANCH into NODE
```

```
            if ST(NODE) = TIME(BRANCH) + ST(node
            at other end of BRANCH)
                then put node at other end of BRANCH
                in set C1
                endif
            enddo
        enddo
endcodesegment
```

16.2   STORING STATIC GRAPHS

If a graph does not change during the course of a computation, it can be stored in a more compact representation by assigning a fixed location to each node and branch and reducing the number of pointers. Let us assume that the number of nodes is N and that the names of the nodes are the integers 1 through N. (If the names are arbitrary values such as character strings, an array of them can be stored; the correspondence between the string and its index in the array provides an integer between 1 and N.) If there is not more than one branch in either direction between any pair of nodes and if no branch connects a node to itself, then the branch data can be stored in a two-dimensional array. For example, TIME(I,J) could be used to store the time required between the start time of node I and the start time of node J. Since the absence of a branch must be represented as well, an impossible value for time must be available: in this example, a negative entry could be used to signify that there is no branch from I to J. This form of representation makes it possible to find any desired branch very rapidly, and if there are connections between most pairs of nodes, this method is probably the best. However, if only a few pairs of nodes are connected (the array is *sparse*), the method is wasteful of storage space, and the operation of finding all branches from a node is slow (since it requires a search through a row of the array).

Another scheme is based on an *access table*, an array that indicates where data can be found. In this example we want to know about the branches into each node. A table of nodes can be constructed, with each entry containing a pointer to a list of branches. Figure 16-8 illustrates this method for the graph shown in Figure 16-7. The entry for node 7, for example, shows that there are three branches coming into node 7, and that the first appears in index position 8 in the arrays TIME and ST_NODE. That is, TIME(8) is the time that must be allotted after the start time of the node at the beginning of the branch, and the number of that node can be found in ST_NODE(8). Information about the three branches is stored in contiguous entries in the branch table, so entries 8, 9, and 10 pertain to node 7. Notice that it is necessary to store the number of incoming branches NIN with each node, to show how many consecutive entries in the branch table pertain to each node.

FIGURE 16-7   Graph represented in Figure 16-8

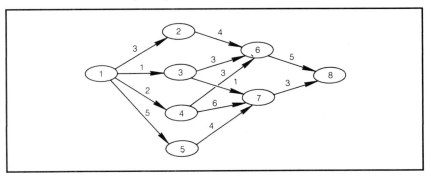

FIGURE 16-8   Static storage for graph in Figure 16-7

Node table			Branch table		
Node	Branches	Access pointers	Branch	TIME	ST_NODE
	NIN	BRANCH_PTR			
1	0	0	1	3	1
2	1	1	2	1	1
3	1	2	3	2	1
4	1	3	4	5	1
5	1	4	5	4	2
6	3	5	6	3	3
7	3	8	7	3	4
8	2	11	8	1	3
			9	6	4
			10	4	5
			11	5	6
			12	3	7

Study of Program 16-1 reveals that additional structure must be im-
posed on the data in storage. During the first phase of the analysis, the
algorithm checks the node at the end of each outgoing branch from a
given node to see whether it can be moved into set U1. (This is done to
avoid a search through the set U for a node that can be moved.) Unfortunately, the present data structure does not make it possible to locate the
outgoing branches from a node easily; in fact, a search of the full branch
table is necessary to find all such branches, and this would take longer

than the time saved by not searching set U. The solution is to form a second branch table of outgoing branches. This requires two more columns in the node table: NOUT, the number of outgoing branches, and OUT_PTR, a pointer to the first entry for the node in the outgoing branch table. The table itself need contain only the number of the node at the other end, END_NODE.

Program 16-1 requires that nodes be placed in various sets. It must be possible to determine whether a node is in set U or set C, and to find a member of set U1 or C1 as fast as possible. Membership in a set can be represented by "marking" a node. An additional column can be added to the node table, and the value in that column can indicate set membership. However, such a method does not make it easy to find a member of a particular set, because the whole column must be searched. It is better to form a list of all the members of a set and to insert and delete members as required. Since the number of nodes is fixed and the node table is fixed in storage, such a list can be constructed through a column of the table. We will use an array MEMBER as a column of the node table to indicate set membership in the following way:

If MEMBER(I) = −1 then node I is in set U.
If MEMBER(I) = −2 then node I is in set C.
If MEMBER(I) > 0 then node I is in set U1, C1, or S.
If node I is in set U1 or C1, then MEMBER(I) is a pointer to the next member of the same set.

Initially, all entries in the node table have MEMBER set to −1. As each node is moved to set U1, MEMBER becomes a positive pointer and remains so while the node is moved from set U1 to S to C1. When a node is moved from set C1 to C, MEMBER is changed to −2. The test to see whether set U is empty after the first phase requires a search through the whole MEMBER column, but this occurs just once in the program. It could be avoided by representing set U as a list, but the additional operations in manipulating the list are not worth the small saving in avoiding the search.

One final idea will be used to implement part of the algorithm efficiently. A *use count* is an integer stored with an entry that gives the number of uses of that entry by other entries. In this problem, we need to know when a node can have its starting time calculated. The calculation is possible when the nodes at the ends of all incoming branches have had their starting times calculated. If a count is available of the number of nodes at the ends of incoming branches whose starting times have been computed, the ability to calculate the starting time of a node can be recognized by the fact that the count is equal to the number of incoming branches. This is best implemented by storing the counter in a column of the node table that is initially set to the number of incoming branches. The counter is then decremented by 1 each time the starting time of a node on an incoming branch is calculated. When the count reaches zero, the node is moved to set U1.

The columns in the three tables for the program are

Node table:	ST	Minimum starting time for node
	NIN	Number of incoming branches
	BRANCH_PTR	Pointer to table of incoming branches
	NOUT	Number of outgoing branches
	OUT_PTR	Pointer to table of outgoing branches
	MEMBER	Set membership code or pointer
	USE	Number of incoming nodes still in set U
Incoming branch table:	ST_NODE	Number of node at other end of branch
	TIME	Delay after completion of ST_NODE
Outgoing branch table:	END_NODE	Number of node at other end of branch

The details of Program 16-1 can now easily be filled in. Since the operation of moving entries into and out of sets U1 and C1 occurs in two places, it is worthwhile to write two very trivial subprograms to insert and remove entries from the front of a list whose start is supplied to the subprogram as a parameter.

PROBLEMS

1 Show that if there is a loop in the graph (it is not acyclic), then the algorithm will leave nodes in set U but will still empty set U1.

2 Show that if the graph is connected and acyclic, all nodes will be moved out of set U.

RANDOM METHODS

■   ■   ■   ■

By *random methods* we do not mean that a method is chosen at random—a problem-solving approach that is about as likely to work as a monkey is to type one of Shakespeare's plays. Rather, we are referring to a class of methods that approximate the solution to a problem by taking many samples "at random" and forming some type of average. This is often done in real life to estimate values that cannot be directly measured. For example, the probability that a roulette wheel will stop on a particular one of its 38 positions is exactly 1/38 if the wheel is *unbiased*—that is, does not favor one outcome over another. About the only way to check that the wheel is unbiased is to spin it many times and count the number of times each outcome occurs. As the number of spins increases, the number of times a particular outcome occurs, divided by the number of spins, gets closer and closer to the probability of that outcome.

Random methods are used in computations in two types of problems. In the first type, the answer could, in principle, be computed exactly, but the computation might be very difficult and time consuming. In some of these problems, random samples can be taken in such a way that the average of many samples approximates the solution. These methods are called Monte Carlo methods and are the subject of the next chapter. In the second type of problem, the answer desired is the characteristic of some random variable. For example, a bank might want to know the average length of the line of people waiting at a teller's window as a result of a proposed organizational change. Obviously, the actual length of the line changes from time to time during the day and is a random variable. One way of measuring the average length would be to make the proposed change and then have somebody stand in the bank measuring the length of the line at regular intervals. This may be both expensive and counterproductive. (If the change causes the length to grow unreasonably, the bank might lose some customers.) An alternative method is to *simulate* the organization on a computer by formulating a mathematical model of the way customers arrive at random and following the behavior of the model on a computer.

To use a random method on a computer, we need a way to generate random numbers that is equivalent to the spin of a roulette wheel or the arrival of customers at a bank. Most computers provide subprograms for generating sequences of numbers that appear to be random. We say "appear to be" because such a sequence is generated by following a prescribed rule that determines the next number from those that have gone before. (We say that the sequence is *deterministic*.) A typical rule used to generate random integers is to multiply the previous integer by a carefully chosen number, and then to extract some of the digits from the result as the next number in the sequence. However, if we ignore the underlying generating procedure, the numbers generated by such a program have all the properties of random numbers. For the purpose of further discussion, we will assume that we have a function subprogram, RANDOM( ), which returns a real value between 0.0 and 1.0, where the probability that the value lies between a and b is $b - a$ for all values $0 \le a < b \le 1$. (RANDOM is a function of no arguments, but we follow it with an empty pair of parentheses to make it clear that it is a function and not a simple variable.)

The next two chapters will illustrate the use of random methods of these two types. The guiding principle in these methods is that we are using a computer to simulate the process of selecting a sample at random.

C H A P T E R

17

The Monte Carlo Method

■　　■　　■　　■　　■　　■　　■

The name *Monte Carlo method* comes from the famous gambling resort. In any game of chance, some device—such as a roulette wheel or a shuffled deck of cards—generates one of a set of random outcomes, and the players bet on that outcome. In roulette, for example, the standard wheel is marked with 38 different numbers, each of which is equally likely to occur when the wheel is spun. Consequently, the *probability* that any given number will come up is 1 in 38. If a player bets on a particular number, the bet will be lost 37 times and won once (on the average). Since the house pays less than 37-to-1 odds for a win, the player is bound to lose if the game is continued long enough, and the house is bound to win. (The house, unlike the player, is not there for the fun of it.) No betting strategy, or "system," can overcome the odds forever; eventually the "law of averages" will catch up with the player.

In statistics, the "law of averages" is called the *law of large numbers*, and states that as the number of bets increases, the likelihood that the outcome will deviate significantly from the *expected outcome* gets smaller and smaller. Thus if the payoff on the roulette wheel is 35 to 1—that is, out of 38 bets the player expects to lose a dollar 37 times and win 35 dollars once—the expected loss to the player is 2/38 of a dollar per play. This is the house profit. Betting on the "reds" does not change this. (Eighteen of the numbers are colored red, and a player can bet on red at even money. That is, if any of the red numbers comes up, a dollar is won; otherwise a dollar is lost.) Since, on the average, 18 of 38 spins will come up red, 18 dollars are won and 20 are lost, for an expected loss of 2/38 of a dollar per play. No matter what combination of bets is made or what the amount of the bets, fixed or varied, in the long run the player will lose 2/38 of the total amount bet (in the sense that the difference between the amount actually lost and this expected loss will get progressively smaller compared with the total amount bet).

This property of random numbers means that they can be used to solve certain types of problem. If we had a game of chance that was more difficult to analyze than roulette, we might consider estimating the probabilities of various outcomes by taking statistics. (Indeed, this may not be a bad idea, even in roulette: it is one way of determining whether the wheel is properly adjusted or has been set to favor the house!)

The *Monte Carlo method* is a method that uses random numbers to solve nonrandom problems. Suppose, for example, that we have a square board with a circle inscribed in it, as shown in Figure 17-1. If we throw darts at this board in such a way that they can land anywhere on the board with equal likelihood, what is the probability that a dart will land inside the circle? Clearly, it is the ratio of the area of the circle to the area of the square: $\pi/4$, or about 0.7854. If we did not know the value of π, we could estimate it by throwing a large number of darts at the board and computing the proportion that land inside the circle. This technique can be implemented on a computer as a way of computing the area of a complex region.

In Chapter 19-1 we will develop several *deterministic* methods for computing areas and apply two of them to the problem of computing the area of a circle. Normally we do not use Monte Carlo, or *probabilistic*, methods when deterministic methods are practical. However, there are some

FIGURE 17-1   Circle inscribed in a square

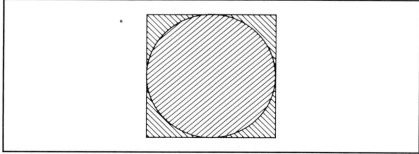

■ Program 17.1   Compute π by Monte Carlo method

```
MONTE_CARLO: program
    The value of π is estimated by taking random samples (X,Y) in a
    unit square and counting the number of samples that lie inside a
    unit circle centered at the origin. The probability that a sample is
    in the unit circle is π/4.
    integer I,M,N,COUNT
    real ESTIMATE,X,Y
        N ← 0
        COUNT ← 0
        output 'INPUT NUMBER OF THROWS TO BE MADE'
        input M
        do while M > 0
            do for I ← 1 to M
                X ← RANDOM()
                Y ← RANDOM()
                if X*X + Y*Y < 1.0 then COUNT ← COUNT + 1
                endif
                enddo
            N ← N + M
            ESTIMATE ← FLOAT(COUNT)/FLOAT(N)*4.0
            output N,ESTIMATE,ESTIMATE - 3.1416
            output 'INPUT NUMBER OF ADDITIONAL THROWS
            TO BE MADE'
            input M
            enddo
    endprogram MONTE_CARLO
```

problems that are very difficult and time consuming to handle deter-
ministically, and for these we must often resort to Monte Carlo methods.
We will illustrate by computing the area of a circle. A computer program
to estimate the value of π by "throwing darts" at Figure 17-1 is given in
Program 17-1. The program expects the user to input an integer representing the number of "darts" to be "thrown." Each throw is simulated by
obtaining two random numbers between 0 and 1, representing the x- and
y-coordinates of the point at which the dart lands. (Since x and y are both
between 0 and 1, the dart always lands in the *positive quadrant*—that is,
the upper right-hand corner—but since the full figure can be constructed
from four identical pieces, the result is not changed. The dart will still
land inside the circle with probability $\pi/4$.) As each position is computed,
a counter is increased by 1 if the position falls inside the circle (that is, if
$x^2 + y^2 < 1.0$). When the number of "throws" requested has been made,
the program prints the estimate of π obtained by taking 4 times the proportion that fall inside the circle. The process may then be repeated for

TABLE 17-1 Sample Output from Program 17-1

N	ESTIMATE	ERROR
100	3.2000	0.0584
200	3.1000	−0.0416
300	3.0267	−0.1149
400	3.0700	−0.0716
500	3.0560	−0.0856
1000	3.0760	−0.0656
2000	3.1380	−0.0036
3000	3.1707	0.0291
4000	3.1570	0.0154
5000	3.1720	0.0304
10000	3.1596	0.0180
20000	3.1580	0.0164
30000	3.1521	0.0105
40000	3.1464	0.0048
50000	3.1536	0.0120
100000	3.1443	0.0027

an additional number of throws. Table 17-1 shows the result of a sample execution of this program. In this table n is the number of "dart throws." Notice that the result approaches the value of π very slowly as n increases. The Monte Carlo method is not a good method to use if direct methods are available; rather, it is used in very complex problems that are difficult to analyze directly and therefore difficult to solve by any other method.

PROBLEMS

1 The earth is an *oblate spheroid*—that is, a sphere flattened at the poles. In this problem we will grossly exaggerate the flattening by assuming that the interior of the earth is the set of points (x, y, z) such that $x^2 + y^2 + 1.2z^2 < 1.0$, where x, y, and z are expressed in units of the earth's equatorial radius (the distance from the center of the earth to the equator, 6.37816×10^6 meters). If points are chosen randomly in the unit cube $0.0 \leq x, y, z \leq 1.0$, then the probability that a point is inside the earth is equal to the volume of the earth divided by the volume of the unit cube. Write a program to estimate the volume of the flattened earth using the Monte Carlo method.

If you want an accurate figure for the volume of the earth, change the coefficient from 1.2 to 1.00674 in the inequality above. The answer must be multiplied by the radius cubed, 2.59469×10^{20}, to get the volume in cubic meters. Unfortunately, an enormous number of samples must be used to get any appreciable accuracy—it is easier to look the answer up! According to the *Encyclopaedia Britannica*, the volume is $1.083218915 \times 10^{21}$ cubic meters.

2 To make a random selection among a small number of possibilities, a random-number generator can be used as follows. Suppose we want to throw a six-sided die to get a result that is equally likely to be any integer between 1 and 6. The value of `1.0 + 6.0*RANDOM()` will be a random real number between 1.0 and 7.0. Truncated to an integer, the result will be one of the integers 1 through 7—though 7 should hardly ever occur. (Many random-number generators generate results *greater than or equal to* zero but strictly *less than* one, so 7 will *never* occur.) If 7 occurs, it should be discarded and another random number generated; in all other cases the result will be the desired random integer. Using this idea, write a program to estimate the probability that a "full house" will be thrown with five dice. (A full house consists of three dice showing the same value, and the other two showing an equal but different value: for example, 3, 5, 3, 3, 5.) At the same time, compute the probability of "three of a kind" (three dice show the same value, but the other two are different).

C H A P T E R

18

Discrete Simulation

■　　　■　　　■　　　■　　　■　　　■

Simulation is a very important tool in many areas of business planning, economics, engineering, and science. In this technique, a model of the real world is analyzed, usually by the computer. A *model* is a set of assumptions about the behavior of a real-world system. For example, it may describe the behavior of an electronic circuit or the expected arrival pattern of customers at a bank. The behavior of the model is studied to determine the effects of various changes without actually making those changes. There are two very different types of simulation in common use, *continuous* and *discrete*. Both forms are intended to predict what will happen to a given system as time passes. Continuous simulation will be the subject of Chapter 20. Its techniques are completely unrelated to the techniques of discrete simulation. In discrete simulation, the model deals with *events* that occur at isolated times—for example, the arrivals of customers at a bank. The model might be used to determine the average waiting time for each customer with various organizations of tellers and lines. In this case, it might be feasible to experiment in a real-world situation; but in a study of, say, the national economy, it is probably better to simulate the effects of a measure such as a tax cut than to try it out in the real world and see what happens.

A significant part of the science (or art) of simulation is the design of an appropriate model. In business simulation, the planner tries to define models that are simple enough to make simulation practical, but comprehensive enough to model all the important effects. Part of the process of simulation is *verification*—comparing the results of simulated and actual experiments to see how well the model agrees with the real world. Only if these results show reasonable agreement can the planner have some degree of faith in the results of further simulations.

Similar considerations apply in science and engineering. If the purpose of a simulation is to design a piece of equipment without having to construct and try out each new design, the model used must be verified by comparing it against some experimental results. In science, simulation is also used to verify or disprove hypotheses. For example, a physicist may hypothesize that certain phenomena behave according to some mathematical equation (model); the simulation either disproves the hypothesis or verifies that it may be true. (It cannot *prove* that it is true!)

Because simulation has been recognized as a valuable tool, there are many programming languages designed especially for simulation applications. When a problem is described in such a *problem-oriented language*, the method of solution does not have to be specified, because it is built into the language processor. GPSS (general purpose system simulation), for example, allows a user to describe a discrete-system model. GPSS interprets the description of the model and simulates its behavior. Thanks to such special-purpose languages, most users of simulation do not need to understand how the simulator itself operates. However, its effective use is enhanced if the principles of simulation are understood. We will take a brief look at the discrete simulation process in this chapter by studying two simple examples.

The majority of discrete simulations deal with random events, and almost all discrete simulation techniques are based on random methods, because even if the events under consideration are not random, it may be impossible to determine them on any other basis. For example, the laws of physics presumably determine when a roulette wheel will stop, for a given initial position and speed. However, these variables are not known precisely, and it is probably not practical to compute the subsequent position of the wheel even if they are known. Similarly, the customers arriving at a bank do not view their arrival times as random; rather, they are determined by the traffic on the way to the bank and other variables, such as the state of the traffic lights. These variables in turn are not random, but are determined by prior events, and so on. However, as far as the bank can observe, the arrival pattern of customers is random and can be treated as such for the purpose of determining its strategy. A bank will therefore choose a random model for customer arrival to plan strategy.

For example, suppose the bank decides that the model will have a customer arriving each minute with probability 1/10. This can be simulated by selecting a random number between 0 and 1 for each simulated minute, and saying that a customer has arrived if the random number is less than 0.1 (because there is a 1/10 chance that the random number will lie between 0.0 and 0.1 rather than between 0.1 and 1.0). In simulation, a *simulated clock* keeps track of the simulated time: with this model, each time the simulated clock advances 1 minute, another random number is obtained to determine whether a customer has arrived.

Example 18.1
Gas Station Waiting Time

Suppose we use this simple model of arrival times for customers at a gas station with one pump, and assume that it takes exactly 8 minutes to serve each customer. How long will each customer have to wait on the average? Although the answer to very simple problems such as this one can be found mathematically, in more complex problems it is necessary to use numerical simulation to find the answer. The numerical simulation of this problem will help us understand some of the techniques.

A program can calculate the average waiting time by computing the waiting time of each customer who arrives, summing those waiting times, and dividing by the number of customers. When the first customer arrives, there is no wait. However, the pump will now be busy for 8 minutes, so any customer who arrives during the next 7 minutes will have to wait until the pump is free. This suggests that we should keep a record of the service time remaining for all customers who have already arrived. In addition, we will need to know the total waiting time for all customers and the number of customers who have arrived. Program 18-1 stores these values in the variables SERVICE, WAIT, and CUST, respectively. For each simulated minute, the program reduces the service time SERVICE by 1 (unless it is already 0) and determines whether another customer has arrived. If so, the wait for that customer is given by SERVICE, so it is added to WAIT, the number of customers is increased by 1, and SERVICE is increased by 8. The simulation model is run for N simulated minutes, supplied as an input parameter.

The simulation can be repeated as many times as desired by providing additional values of N. It is terminated by giving a zero value for N. The reason for running the simulation more than once is to compare results. Since arrivals are random, each simulation may yield a different answer. If the simulation has been run for a suitably long time, the result will be close to the expected waiting time; but if it is run for only a short time, the result may be very different. When multiple runs of a simulation are made to compare answers in this way, it is important not to restart the program simply by resubmitting it to the computer. The random-number

■ Program 18.1   Simple simulation model of a gas station

```
GAS: program
    Compute the average waiting time of customers at a gas station that
    takes 8 minutes to service each customer. Customers arrive each
    minute with a probability of 0.1.
    real AVERAGE_WAIT,RANDOM
    integer N,WAIT,SERVICE,CUST,TIME
        input N
        SERVICE ← 0
        do while N > 0
            WAIT ← 0
            CUST ← 0
            do for TIME ← 1 to N
                SERVICE ← MAX(SERVICE - 1,0)
                if RANDOM() ≥ 0.9
                    then
                        CUST ← CUST + 1
                        WAIT ← WAIT + SERVICE
                        SERVICE ← SERVICE + 8
                    endif
                enddo
            AVERAGE_WAIT ← FLOAT(WAIT)/FLOAT(CUST)
            output 'AVERAGE WAIT FOR', N, 'CUSTOMERS
            IS', AVERAGE_WAIT
            input N
            enddo
    endprogram GAS
```

generator, RANDOM( ) in this program, does not actually produce random numbers: it produces numbers that are in a sequence that *appears* to be random. If the sequence is begun from the same place, the same results will be obtained. Most random-number generators have provisions for starting at different points in the sequence, but the details are machine- and language-dependent and will not be discussed here.

Simulation methods of the sort used in Example 18-1 are very simple to design, because the computer program is simply modeling all the important variables in the physical system being studied and keeping track of them in time. There is no question of finding a method: it is just a question of mimicking on the computer the way we would get the answer if we measured the answer at the gas station itself (in this example) by keeping track of the number of people waiting throughout a day. The complications that arise in this type of simulation are due only to the desire to get more realistic models by introducing additional factors.

Program 18-1 uses a very simple model for the arrival times of customers. A more realistic model is based on *interarrival times*, the times between consecutive customer arrivals. The model might assume, for instance, that the time between two consecutive arrivals is a random number between 0.5 and 4.5 minutes, with any time being equally likely. (In practice, the assumption is that the interarrival time may be any time greater than 0, with shorter times being more probable than longer times; but this involves the theory of random distributions, a topic beyond the scope of this text.) If we want to construct a random number with values that are equally likely between any pair of values, we can use the random-number generator to generate a number between 0 and 1, and convert that range to the desired range. For example, we can generate a random number between 0.5 and 4.5 by computing `0.5 + (4.5 - 0.5)*RANDOM()`.

Example 18.2
Bank Line Simulation

In this example we will use interarrival times for customers arriving at the drive-up windows of a bank. Suppose the bank managers are trying to decide how to lay out the approaches to their two drive-up windows. The alternatives are to provide two separate drives, one for each window, or a single drive feeding both windows. In the former case, a customer has to decide which line to join on arrival; in the latter case, the customer joins the single line, and, after arriving at the head of the line, takes the next available window. It is fairly obvious that the latter solution will lead to an average wait no longer than the former, and might lead to shorter waits, because there will be times when a customer joins one line only to find that the other line becomes empty sooner. However, if the latter solution is going to cost a little more, the bank managers may wish to determine the effect on the average wait to see whether the extra cost is justified. They may also want to measure some other statistics. For example, the customer's unhappiness increases more rapidly as the wait gets longer, so the managers may want to measure the average of the *square* of the waiting time. This will give an indication of the amount of variation in the waiting times: if the average of the squares is much larger than the square of the average waiting time, then there is a lot of variation in the waiting times for different customers.

In preparing a model for simulation, the bank managers must first determine the pattern of arrivals and service times for each customer. They do this by measuring the average number of customers arriving at various times of the day and the average length of time taken to service each customer. Let us suppose that these measurements have been taken, and that we know the bank can expect customers to arrive randomly, with interarrival times between 2 and 6 minutes, and that service time is also random, between 1 and 10 minutes. To avoid complications, we will also assume that these random numbers are *uniformly distributed*—that is, that any value in the range is equally likely. With this much data, the bank managers can now ask, What is the average waiting time and the average square of the waiting time for the two arrangements? The solution can be found by simulation.

Simulations of this type deal with *events*. An event in this case is the arrival of a customer or the completion of service for a customer. When an event occurs, the *state* of the system changes. When a customer arrives, the number of customers in line changes; when a teller completes the service of a customer, that customer leaves the system, and if there are customers waiting in line for that teller, a customer moves from the line for service. The basic action of the simulator is to keep track of the times at which events can occur, and advance the simulated clock to the next event time. For example, if the next customer is due to arrive in 2.6 minutes, but the next time that a teller will complete service is 3.5 minutes, the clock must be advanced 2.6 minutes and a new customer added to the line. A random number is then generated to determine when the next customer will arrive. If the time before the next arrival is 4.2 minutes, the next event will be the completion of service by a teller. The clock is advanced again and the next customer is removed from the waiting line. The service time for that customer determines the time of the next event concerning that teller. In this problem we must keep track of three event times: the time of the next customer arrival and the times at which each of the tellers will complete the service of a customer. The simplest way to do this is to store the time at which each event will occur relative to the start of the simulation—that is, the simulated clock should be set to zero at the start of the simulation, and event times specified in minutes after that time. Figures 18-1a and 18-1b illustrate the two arrangements to be considered in this simulation. The assumption in the two-line system is that an arriving customer will choose the shorter line.

The basic structure of the simulation program consists of a loop that advances simulated time, held in the variable `TIME`, to the next event time and processes this event. The loop must be terminated by some mechanism. In this case, as in most simulations, we want to stop after some specified elapsed simulation time, which we hope will be long enough to give meaningful statistics. An outline of the program is shown in Program 18-2. This program inputs a parameter specifying the length of the simulated run. Subsequent inputs cause further simulations, which start from the state left by the previous run—that is, there may be customers in line and being served when a simulation begins. Unless the first run is very long, the initial start-up may bias the results, because it may take a while for the lines to build up to their normal length. Therefore, it is a good idea to run the simulation for a while to allow the lines to build up, but to ignore the results from that part of the run.

FIGURE 18-1A   One-line system for two-teller bank

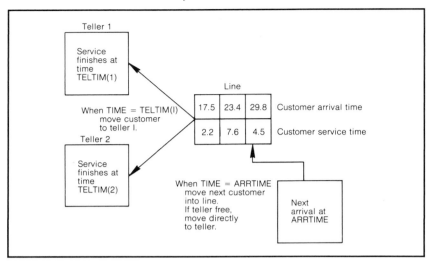

FIGURE 18-1B   Two-line system for two-teller bank

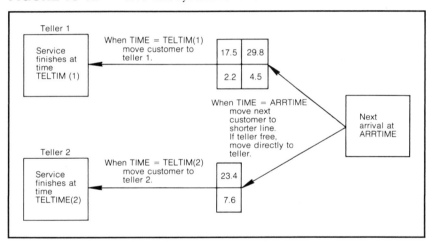

Program 18-2 does not address the problem of how to store information about customers in the line or lines, nor does it consider how to indicate that a teller is not busy. The latter problem can be handled in two ways: we can use either a flag to indicate whether each teller is free or a value of `TELTIM` that would not otherwise be used. Using special values of variables frequently leads to shorter programs, but not necessarily to programs that are easy to follow. Therefore, we will use the first method: we introduce the logical array `BUSY`, which is **true** in position *I* if teller *I* is busy and **false** otherwise.

■ Program 18.2   Outline of bank simulation

```
BANK: program
    A two-teller bank is simulated to compute expected wait times and
    squared wait times.
    real TELTIM(2),TIME,ARRTIME,STOPTIME,LENGTH,
    WAIT,WAITSQ
    integer NCUSTS
        initialize tellers and lines to empty
        input LENGTH
        TIME ← 0.0
        do while LENGTH > 0.0
            STOPTIME ← TIME + LENGTH
            WAIT ← 0.0
            WAITSQ ← 0.0
            NCUSTS ← 0
            do while TIME < STOPTIME
                find earliest event from ARRTIME and
                TELTIM(I), I = 1,2
                if next event is an arrival
                    then
                        TIME ← ARRTIME
                        handle new arrival
                    else
                        TIME ← TELTIM(I)
                        handle completion for teller I
                    endif
            enddo
            output WAIT/FLOAT(NCUSTS),WAITSQ/FLOAT
            (NCUSTS)
            input LENGTH
        enddo
    endprogram BANK

handle completion for teller I: subprogram
    (declarations)
        if customer waiting for this teller
            then
                move customer to teller from line
                TELTIM(I) ← TIME + service time for
                this customer
                WAIT ← WAIT + TIME − customer arrival
                time
                WAITSQ ← WAITSQ + (TIME − customer
                arrival time) ↑ 2
                NCUSTS ← NCUSTS + 1
                mark teller I as busy
```

```
        else
            mark teller I as not busy
        endif
    return
    endsubprogram handle completion for teller I
handle new arrival: subprogram
    (declarations)
        compute time of next arrival and assign to
        ARRTIME
        compute service time
        add to line (or to shorter line if two-line
        system)
        if teller I free for I = 1 or 2
            then handle completion for teller I
            endif
    return
    endsubprogram handle new arrival
```

The problem of storing information about customers requires more thought. As customers enter the system, we must keep a record of their arrival times and the time it will take to service them. The number of customers waiting will vary during the simulation, and in the two-line system there can be more customers in one line than in the other. This is a common situation in simulation: as *entities* (in this example, customers) move through the system, they must be saved in lines waiting to be processed by the next stage. In this example there is only one stage, the teller; but in a model of an automobile assembly plant, for example, there may be many stages, representing the different processes that must be completed in the manufacture of a car. The best mechanism for keeping track of the customers in a line is the *chained list* introduced in Chapter 3. Each customer becomes one entry in a list representing the line. One list head is needed for each line, but if there are two lines, both lists can be stored in one set of arrays. The lists in this problem must contain two data items, customer arrival time and service time, so three arrays are needed— CUSTAR, SERVTM, and PTR—for the two times and a pointer. PTR(1) and PTR(2) can be used as the list heads for the lines for tellers 1 and 2 in the two-line system.

Program 18-3 gives a complete program for the simulation of the two-line system. It uses the declaration **global** to indicate that variables are known in all subprograms. The changes needed to simulate a one-line version are small: the first executable statement in the subprogram TELLER should be changed from K ← I to K ← 1, and the statement containing **if** QLENGTH(2) . . . should be removed from the subprogram ARRIVAL.

```
BANK: program
```
   A two-teller bank is simulated to compute expected waiting times.
   Variables used include

`TELTIM(I)`	*Time at which teller* I *will next be free*
`ARRTIME`	*Time at which next customer will arrive*
`BUSY(I)`	*Teller* I *is busy if true*
`QLENGTH(I)`	*Number of customers waiting for teller* I *including one at window*
`PTR,CUSTAR,SERVTM`	*Storage for list structure containing pointers, arrival times, and service times of customers*
`PTR(I), I = 1, 2`	*List heads for lines 1 and 2*
`LEND(I)`	*Ends of lists for lines 1 and 2*
`FREE`	*Start of free list in list structure*

```
       real TELTIM(2),TIME,ARRTIME,STOPTIME,
       LENGTH,WAIT,WAITSQ,CUSTAR(100),
       SERVTM(100),T
       integer QLENGTH(2),LEND(2),PTR(100),FREE,
       I,NCUSTS
       logical BUSY(2)
       global BUSY,TELTIM,ARRTIME,QLENGTH,PTR,
       CUSTAR,SERVTM,LEND,FREE,TIME,WAIT,WAITSQ,
       NCUSTS
           call INITIALIZE
           input LENGTH
           TIME ← 0.0
           do while LENGTH > 0.0
               STOPTIME ← TIME + LENGTH
               WAIT ← 0.0
               WAITSQ ← 0.0
               NCUSTS ← 0
               do while TIME < STOPTIME
                   T ← ARRTIME
                   I ← 0
                   if T > TELTIM(1) and BUSY(1)
                       then
                           I ← 1
                           T ← TELTIM(1)
                       endif
                   if T > TELTIM(2) and BUSY(2) then
                   I ← 2 endif
                   if I = 0
                       then
```

```
                              TIME ← ARRTIME
                              call ARRIVAL
                          else
                              TIME ← TELTIM(I)
                              call TELLER(I)
                          endif
                      enddo
                  output 'NUMBER OF CUSTOMERS,AVERAGE
                  WAIT,AND AVERAGE SQUARE WAIT'
                  output NCUSTS, WAIT/FLOAT(NCUSTS),
                  WAITSQ/
                  FLOAT(NCUSTS)
                  input LENGTH
                  enddo
          endprogram BANK
      TELLER: subprogram (I)
          Called if Teller I has just completed a customer,
          or is free and a customer has just been added to
          line K.
          (all global declarations from main program)
          integer I,J,K
              K ← I
              if BUSY(I) then QLENGTH(K) ← QLENGTH(K) − 1
              endif
              if PTR(K) ≠ 0
                  then
                      J ← PTR(K)
                      PTR(K) ← PTR(J)
                      TELTIM(I) ← TIME + SERVTM(J)
                      WAIT ← WAIT + TIME − CUSTAR(J)
                      WAITSQ ← WAITSQ + (TIME −
                      CUSTAR(J)) ↑ 2
                      NCUSTS ← NCUSTS + 1
                      BUSY(I) ← true
                      if PTR(K) = 0 then LEND(K) ← K endif
                      Return J to free storage.
                      PTR(J) ← FREE
                      FREE ← J
                  else
                      BUSY(I) ← false
                  endif
              return
          endsubprogram TELLER
      ARRIVAL: subprogram
          Handle new arrival. Compute service times and time of next arrival
          and add new customer to line. If no free space available, force
          TIME past stop time.
```

```
(all global declarations from main program)
integer I,J
real RANDOM
    if FREE = 0
        then
            output 'NO FREE SPACE LEFT, SIMULATION
            ABANDONED'
            TIME ← 1.0E50
        else
            I ← FREE
            FREE ← PTR(I)
            ARRTIME ← TIME + 2.0 + 4.0*RANDOM()
            SERVTM(I) ← 1.0 + 9.0*RANDOM()
            J ← 1
            if QLENGTH(2) < QLENGTH(1) then J ← 2
            endif
            Add to line J.
            QLENGTH(J) ← QLENGTH(J) + 1
            PTR(I) ← 0
            CUSTAR(I) ← TIME
            PTR(LEND(J)) ← I
            LEND(J) ← I
            if not BUSY(1)
                then call TELLER(1)
                else if not BUSY(2) then call
                TELLER(2) endif
                endif
        endif
    return
endsubprogram ARRIVAL
INITIALIZE: subprogram
    (all global declarations from main program)
    integer I
        do for I ← 1 to 2
            LEND(I) ← I
            PTR(I) ← 0
            QLENGTH(I) ← 0
            BUSY(I) ← false
        enddo
        do for I ← 3 to 99
            PTR(I) ← I + 1
        enddo
        PTR(100) ← 0
        FREE ← 3
        ARRTIME ← 0.0
        return
    endsubprogram INITIALIZE
```

PROBLEM

1 Program 18-3 uses lists to store the line(s) of waiting customers. These lists are manipulated in subprograms `TELLER` and `ARRIVAL`: the former removes an element from a list and returns the space to the free list, the latter gets space from the free list and adds an element to a list of customers. In general, it is not good programming practice to manipulate lists in subprograms whose principal task is something else. In this case, `TELLER` is principally concerned with simulating the action of the teller, and `ARRIVAL` with the arrival process. Therefore, Program 18-3 should be organized differently: separate subprograms should be written to add an element to the end of a list and to remove an element from the front of a list. These subprograms can then be called from `ARRIVAL` and `TELLER`, respectively. (This organization also has the advantage that, when additional aspects of the bank's operation need to be simulated, the list-manipulation subprograms are available for use by other modules.)

Rewrite the subprograms `TELLER` and `ARRIVAL` following this superior organization. (Notice that `ARRIVAL` has to take care of the difficulty that arises when there is no space in the free list. Since the simulation cannot continue in this case, the subprogram prints an error message and then forces termination by advancing `TIME` to a value larger than any value that will be used. This is a decision that should be made in the subprogram `ARRIVAL`, not in a list-manipulation subprogram, since there could be other procedures calling the list-manipulation subprogram that want to take some action other than terminating the process when there is no free space left.)

P A R T

VI

INTEGRATION

■   ■   ■   ■

The use of a computer to solve problems that involve integration is very important in many application areas. Although a mathematical understanding of this topic requires a knowledge of calculus, simple problems can be tackled without that background. Many problems cannot be solved exactly by computer. For these problems only a numerical approximation can be formed, and such numerical approximations can often be derived by common-sense application of simple principles without any knowledge of calculus. In this part we will look at the two forms of integration problems that arise frequently. The first is the type of problem in which we wish to approximate a value such as the area of a figure whose sides are curved. Computation of a value for such a problem is called *quadrature*. The second type of problem arises when we wish to determine what happens to an object that is subject to certain influences over a period of time. For example, we might know the thrust of a rocket and wish to know the path the rocket will take, or we might be told how the rate of consumption of various supplies depends on the population and other supplies and wish to know what will happen to the availability of the supplies and the population in the future. (Those of you who have had calculus will realize that we are talking about differential equations and that the computer problem is to form an approximate integral.) This type of problem is at the center of *continuous simulation*, which is the problem of determining how a system behaves over a period of time.

19

Quadrature

■ ■ ■ ■ ■ ■ ■

A numerical problem that frequently has to be solved on a computer is that of *numerical quadrature*: finding the area or volume of an object whose shape is known. This problem can arise in relatively simple situations such as the design of freeways, where it is necessary to know how much earth must be removed or filled in to bring the roadbed to the desired level, or in more complex problems such as airplane design, where the area of the wing affects (for example) the viscous drag. In this chapter we will briefly discuss the problem of computing numerical approximations to the areas of two-dimensional (that is, flat) objects. The extension of these results to computation of the surface areas and volumes of three-dimensional (that is, solid) objects is not simple, but the basic ideas are similar.

Suppose we have a closed figure such as that shown in Figure 19-1, and we want to find its area. One method, which is often learned in grade school, is to draw squares over the figure and count the number of squares, as shown in Figure 19-2. Suppose these squares are each 1 foot on a side. The squares shaded ▨ are completely inside the figure. There are 10 of them, so the area is certainly no less than 10 square feet.

FIGURE 19-1   Closed figure

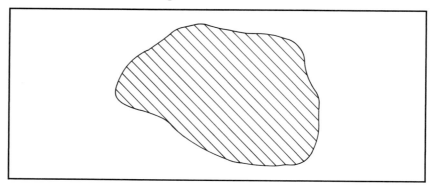

FIGURE 19-2   "Squares" method for finding area

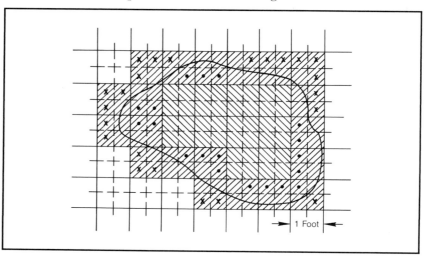

The squares shaded 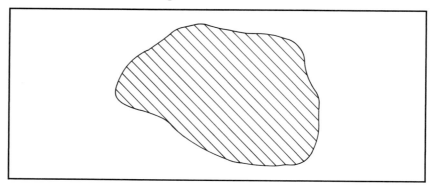 are partly inside and partly outside the figure: we will call these the *boundary squares*. There are 20 such squares, so the area of the figure is not more than 30 square feet (the sum of all the shaded squares). Thus we have the numerical result

$$10 \leq \text{area} \leq 30$$

Not a very precise estimate! How can we get more precision if we need it? One way is to use smaller squares. In Figure 19-2 we have also sub-divided each square with dashed lines into 4 smaller squares. In this process the original 10 one-foot squares that were inside the figure have become 40 six-inch squares, all inside the figure. In addition we have another 19 six-inch squares (those with dots in their centers) that were previously part of the boundary squares and are now completely inside the figure. Thus the area of the figure is no less than $(10 \times 4 + 19)/4$ square feet. Of the remaining six-inch squares formed from the old one-foot boundary squares, 23 (those with x's in their centers) are now completely outside the figure. Thus the area is no greater than $(30 \times 4 - 23)/4$ square feet. We now have the numerical result

$$14.75 \leq \text{area} \leq 24.25$$

The uncertainty is still not very small, but it has improved by a factor of more than 2 (from 20 to 9.5). We can get more precision by making the squares even smaller.

We naturally wonder whether we can get as much precision as we like by making the squares as small as necessary. For this problem, the answer is yes (provided that the boundary line of the figure is reasonably smooth). In fact, for each factor of 2 (or any number α) by which we decrease the side of the squares, the uncertainty will decrease by about the same factor. We can see this intuitively when we realize that the boundary squares will always include the boundary line of the original figure, and therefore form a "thick line" representation of the boundary that is about as thick as the squares. If the side of the squares is reduced, so is the thickness of the line. The area of the thick line is precisely the uncertainty and is roughly proportional to the thickness of the line—that is, to the side of the squares.

FIGURE 19-3   Total error

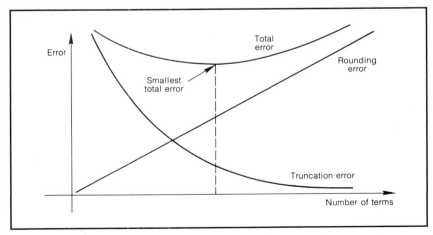

The property that as we successively refine a process by taking more and more terms (in this example, squares) we get closer and closer to the true value is called *convergence*. Usually we try to use convergent processes, so that we can get as much precision as desired; but we must remember that the more terms we use, the more rounding errors will occur. Hence the sum of all the rounding errors will increase as the truncation error decreases. The total error is the sum of the two errors, as shown in Figure 19-3. We can see from the figure that the total error will initially decrease to a minimum, then increase again as the rounding error becomes dominant.

The measurement of an area by counting squares is about the crudest approximation we can use, but it does have the important property of convergence. Before investigating other methods, we will simplify the problem somewhat. In Figure 19-4 we have chopped the original figure up into five pieces with vertical and horizontal lines. The piece shaded diagonally is a rectangle, whose area can be calculated directly by multiplication. The remaining four pieces all have the general shape shown in Figure 19-5.

If we knew how to find the areas of regions like that in Figure 19-5, we could find the area of Figure 19-4 by adding up the areas of the five sub-

FIGURE 19-4   Division of region into subregions

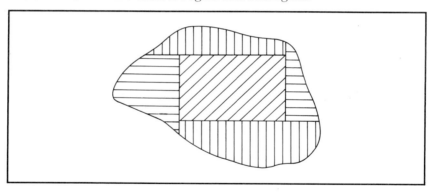

FIGURE 19-5   General shape of remaining subregions

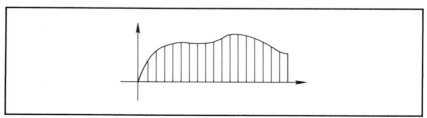

FIGURE 19-6   Definite integral of $f(x)$ between A and B

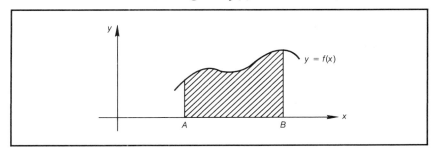

FIGURE 19-7   Using squares and rectangles to determine area

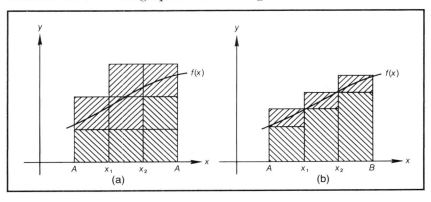

regions. Therefore we will study the restricted problem of finding the area below a curve $y = f(x)$ between the lines $x = A$ and $x = B$, as shown in Figure 19-6. This area is called the *definite integral of $f(x)$ between A and B*, and is written as

$$\int_A^B f(x)\ dx$$

If we put squares on Figure 19-6, we would be counting an integer number of squares to estimate the area, as shown in Figure 19-7a. Suppose, instead, that we use rectangles of the same width as the squares, but with heights determined by the function $f(x)$, as shown in Figure 19-7b. We can calculate the area of the rectangles easily, and we can see that we will get at least as much precision. In Figure 19-7a the boundary region representing the uncertainty consists of four squares, whereas in Figure 19-7b it consists of three rectangles, each smaller than the corresponding square.

19.1 TRAPEZOIDAL RULE

We have shown the interval $[A, B]$ chopped up into three smaller intervals in Figure 19-7. Let us write x_0 for A and x_3 for B. The rectangles all have the same width; let us call it h. Thus

$$x_1 - x_0 = x_2 - x_1 = x_3 - x_2 = h$$

or

$$x_n = x_0 + nh \quad \text{for} \quad n = 0, 1, 2, \ldots$$

The area shaded 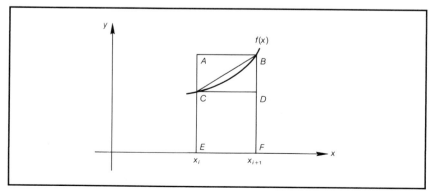 in Figure 19-7b consists of three rectangles. The height of the first is $f(x_0)$; the heights of the second and third are $f(x_1)$ and $f(x_2)$, respectively. Thus the total area, which is the sum of the areas of the three rectangles, is

$$(x_1 - x_0) f(x_0) + (x_2 - x_1) f(x_1) + (x_3 - x_2) f(x_2)$$
$$= h[f(x_0) + f(x_1) + f(x_2)]$$

This is less than the area under the curve $f(x)$ in Figure 19-7.

Similarly, the total shaded area in Figure 19-7b, which is larger than the area under $f(x)$, is given by

$$(x_1 - x_0) f(x_1) + (x_2 - x_1) f(x_2) + (x_3 - x_2) f(x_3)$$
$$= h[f(x_1) + f(x_2) + f(x_3)]$$

Since the first of these expressions is smaller than the actual area and the second is larger, we can take as a better approximation the average of the two. Thus we estimate the area as

FIGURE 19-8   Trapezoidal rule

$$\frac{1}{2}\Big[h[f(x_0) + f(x_1) + f(x_2)] + h[f(x_1) + f(x_2) + f(x_3)]\,\Big]$$

$$= \frac{h}{2}[f(x_0) + 2f(x_1) + 2f(x_2) + f(x_3)]$$

What are we really doing when we take the average of the two approximations? Figure 19-8 shows one of the rectangular regions. The smaller approximation uses the rectangular region $CDFE$, the larger uses $ABFE$. The larger, $ABFE$, is composed of $CDFE$ and $ABDC$. Thus the average of the two areas is

$$\frac{1}{2}[\text{area}(ABFE) + \text{area}(CDFE)]$$

$$= \frac{1}{2}[(\text{area}(CDFE) + \text{area}(ABDC)) + \text{area}(CDFE)]$$

$$= \text{area}(CDFE) + \frac{1}{2}\text{area}(ABDC)$$

Half the area of $ABDC$ is the area of the triangle BDC. Thus the average is the same as the area of the trapezoid $CBFE$, and our approximation is the area under CB, the *straight-line approximation* to the graph of $f(x)$ through C and B. This area is given by

$$\frac{(x_{i+1} - x_i)}{2}[f(x_i) + f(x_{i+1})] = \frac{h}{2}[f(x_i) + f(x_{i+1})]$$

This is called the *trapezoidal rule* for approximate quadrature.

We can take any interval, such as AB in Figure 19-6, chop it into subintervals, and apply the trapezoidal rule to each subinterval. For example, if we chop AB into three subintervals by dividing it at x_1 and x_2, we get

$$\text{area} \cong \frac{h}{2}[f(x_0) + f(x_1)] + \frac{h}{2}[f(x_1) + f(x_2)] + \frac{h}{2}[f(x_2) + f(x_3)]$$

$$= \frac{h}{2}[f(x_0) + 2f(x_1) + 2f(x_2) + f(x_3)]$$

as above. Similarly, if we chop the interval into N subintervals of length $h = (B - A)/N$, we get the approximation

$$\text{area} \cong \frac{h}{2}[f(x_0) + 2f(x_1) + 2f(x_2) + \cdots + 2f(x_{N-1}) + f(x_N)]$$

This method is also *convergent*—that is, as we make N larger, the approximation gets closer to the actual area.

Example 19.1

Area of a Circle by the Trapezoidal Rule

We wish to compute the area of a circle of radius 1. It can be divided into four equal segments and a square, as shown in Figure 19-9. Since the diagonal of the square is twice the radius of the circle, the side of the square is $\sqrt{2}$. Its area is therefore $(\sqrt{2})^2 = 2$. The areas of the four segments must be approximated by numerical integration. One segment is shown in Figure 19-10. The equation of the curved boundary is $(y + \sqrt{2}/2)^2 + x^2 = 1$, because the center is at $x = 0$, $y = -\sqrt{2}/2$ (the point O in the figure).

Because AB, the side of the square, is $\sqrt{2}$, the point A is $(x = -\sqrt{2}/2, y = 0)$, and the point B is $(x = +\sqrt{2}/2, y = 0)$. V is the point $(x = 0, y = 1 - \sqrt{2}/2)$. The midpoints of AQ and QB are also shown. P is $(x = -\sqrt{2}/4, y = 0)$ and R is $(x = \sqrt{2}/4, y = 0)$. Hence U and W have a y-coordinate of $\sqrt{7/8} - \sqrt{2}/2$.

FIGURE 19-9　　Five subregions of a circle

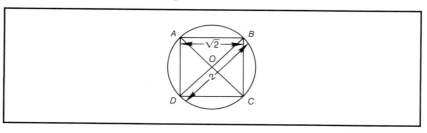

FIGURE 19-10　　One segment of the circle $y = \sqrt{1 - x^2} - \sqrt{2}/2$

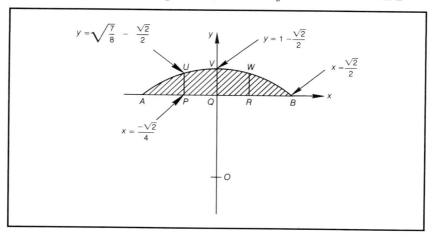

We will apply the trapezoidal rule, first to the two intervals AQ and QB, then to the four intervals AP, PQ, QR, and RB. The approximate area of the circle will then be 4 times our approximation to the area of the segment plus the area of the square, which we know to be 2.

Approximating with two intervals,

$$\text{area} \cong \frac{AQ}{2}\,[y(A) + 2y(V) + y(B)]$$

$$= \frac{\sqrt{2}}{4}\,(0 + 2 - \sqrt{2} + 0) = 0.207$$

This leads to an approximation of $2 + 4 \times 0.207 = 2.828$ for the area of the circle.

Repeating the calculation with four intervals,

$$\text{area} \cong \frac{AP}{2}\,[y(A) + 2y(U) + 2y(V) + 2y(W) + y(B)]$$

$$= \frac{\sqrt{2}}{8}\,[0 + 2(\sqrt{7/8} - \sqrt{2}/2) + 2(1 - \sqrt{2}/2)$$

$$+ 2(\sqrt{7/8} - \sqrt{2}/2) + 0]$$

$$= \frac{\sqrt{2}}{8}\,(4\sqrt{7/8} - 2\sqrt{2} + 2 - \sqrt{2})$$

$$= 0.265$$

This gives an approximation to the area of the circle of $2 + 4 \times 0.265 = 3.060$.

The area of a circle of radius 1 is $\pi \cong 3.142$. Thus the errors are $3.142 - 2.828 = 0.314$ for the two-interval case, and $3.142 - 3.060 = 0.082$ for the four-interval case. When we used the square-counting method, we saw that halving the size of the squares just about halved the error. This time we see that, with the trapezoidal rule, the error is divided by about four when the interval is halved. If we halve the interval again, the error is about 0.022.

19.2 SIMPSON'S RULE

Simpson's rule is another, more accurate method for approximating areas. We will derive it intuitively from the trapezoidal rule, without going into any theory. Simpson's rule is applicable to many problems, and is the basis of many numerical-quadrature programs available in computer libraries. If you ever need to perform numerical quadrature, consider using one of these library programs. You should not attempt to write your own

FIGURE 19-11   Simpson's rule

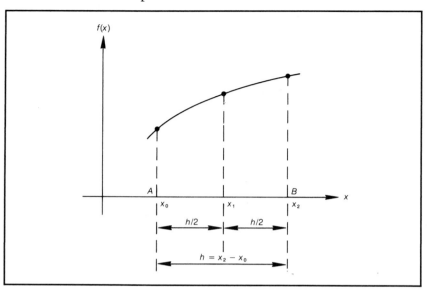

program for problems of this type unless there are very good reasons why the library versions are not applicable to your program; carefully developed library programs are much more likely to be error-free and to look after some of the messy details that we cannot discuss in an introductory presentation.

We commented at the end of the previous section that the error in the trapezoidal rule decreases by approximately one-fourth when the number of intervals is doubled. Consider two numerical approximations to the integral of $f(x)$ over the interval AB, first using one interval and then using two half-length intervals, as shown in Figure 19-11. Let us call these approximations A_1 and A_2. They are

$$A_1 = \text{trapezoidal rule using one interval of length } h = x_2 - x_0$$

$$= \frac{h}{2}\,[f(x_0) + f(x_2)]$$

$$A_2 = \text{trapezoidal rule using two intervals of length } h/2$$

$$= \frac{h}{4}\,[f(x_0) + 2f(x_1) + f(x_2)]$$

Suppose that the error in A_2 is e—that is,

$$A_2 = \text{area} + e$$

Since the error in A_1 is about 4 times the error in A_2, we have the approximation

$$A_1 = \text{area} + 4e$$

If we ignore the fact that the last equation is only an approximation, we can solve the two equations

$$A_1 = \text{area} + 4e$$
$$A_2 = \text{area} + e$$

for the unknown area and hope to obtain a better approximation than we can get by the trapezoidal rule. By subtracting 4 times the second equation from the first and dividing by -3, we obtain

$$\text{area} = (4A_2 - A_1)/3$$

Replacing the values of A_1 and A_2 with the expressions given above, we get

$$\text{area} = \frac{h}{6}[f(x_0) + 4f(x_1) + f(x_2)]$$

This is called *Simpson's rule* for approximate quadrature.

As with the trapezoidal rule, we can break an interval up into many subintervals and apply Simpson's rule to each one. Thus, if we choose $h = (B - A)/N$ and $x_{i+1} - x_i = h/2$, with $x_0 = A$ and $x_{2N} = B$, we have

$$\int_A^B f(x)\, dx = \text{area under curve } f(x) \text{ between } A \text{ and } B$$

$$= \text{area under curve } f(x) \text{ between } x_0 \text{ and } x_2$$
$$+ \text{ area under curve between } x_2 \text{ and } x_4$$
$$+ \cdots$$
$$+ \text{ area under curve between } x_{2N-2} \text{ and } x_{2N}$$

$$\cong \frac{h}{6}[f(x_0) + 4f(x_1) + f(x_2)]$$

$$+ \frac{h}{6}[f(x_2) + 4f(x_3) + f(x_4)]$$

$$+ \cdots$$

$$+ \frac{h}{6}[f(x_{2N-2}) + 4f(x_{2N-1}) + f(x_{2N})]$$

$$= \frac{h}{6}[f(x_0) + 4f(x_1) + 2f(x_2) + 4f(x_3) + 2f(x_4)$$

$$+ \cdots + 2f(x_{2N-2}) + 4f(x_{2N-1}) + f(x_{2N})]$$

Example 19.2
Area of a Circle by Simpson's Rule

We will use Simpson's rule to calculate the area of a unit circle. As before, we break the circle into a square of area 2 and four equal segments like the one in Figure 19-10.

First we use the single interval AB shown in Figure 19-10.

$$\text{area} \cong \frac{\sqrt{2}}{6} \left[y(A) + 4y(V) + y(B) \right]$$

$$= \frac{\sqrt{2}}{6} \left[0 + 4 - 2\sqrt{2} + 0 \right]$$

$$= 0.276$$

This gives the numerical approximation to the area of the circle as $2 + 4 \times 0.276 = 3.104$.

■ Program 19.1   Integration by Simpson's rule

```
INTEGRATION: subprogram (A,B,F,N)
    The real function F is integrated over the interval (A,B) using
    Simpson's rule. The interval is divided into N equal subintervals.
    real A,B,INTEGRATION,F,H,H2,SUM1,SUM2,X,Z
    integer I,N
       if N ≤ 0
          then
              output 'INTEGRATION CALLED WITH N ≤ 0'
              Z = 0.0
          else
              H ← (B - A)/FLOAT(N)
              H2 ← H/2.0
              SUM1 ← 0.0
              SUM2 ← F(A + H2)
              do for I ← 1 to N - 1
                  X ← A + I*H
                  SUM1 ← SUM1 + F(X)
                  SUM2 ← SUM2 + F(X + H2)
                  enddo
              Z ← H*(F(A) + 2.0*SUM1
                + F(B) + 4.0*SUM2)/6.0
          endif
       return (Z)
    endsubprogram INTEGRATION
```

Next we use the two intervals AQ and QB to get

$$\text{area} \cong \frac{\sqrt{2}}{12} \left[y(A) + 4y(U) + 2y(V) + 4y(W) + y(B) \right]$$

$$= \frac{\sqrt{2}}{12} \left[0 + 4\sqrt{7/8} - 2\sqrt{2} + 2 - \sqrt{2} + 4\sqrt{7/8} - 2\sqrt{2} + 0 \right]$$

$$\cong 0.2843$$

This gives a numerical approximation to the area of the circle of $2 + 4 \times 0.2843 = 3.1372$. The errors in the two cases are about 0.038 and 0.0044. The time the error has been divided by about 9. If we divided the interval into two again, we would find that the error decreases by about 16 each time the interval is halved, once the interval is small enough.

Program 19-1 is a function subprogram that computes an approximation to the integral of the function f, using Simpson's rule on the interval (A, B) divided into N equal subintervals. The parameter F is the name of a function that computes the value f.

PROBLEMS

1 Write a function subprogram that takes the same parameters as Program 19-1, but uses the trapezoidal rule to compute the approximation.

2 Many numerical programs for problems that cannot be solved exactly are *adaptive*. An adaptive program automatically chooses some of the optional parameters that determine the accuracy of the method. An *adaptive quadrature* program automatically chooses the subinterval size used. One way to do this is to apply the method twice, once with a subinterval size of h equal to the interval (a, b) and then with two subintervals of size $h/2$. The difference between the results can be used as an estimate of the error. If the error estimate is too large, the process can be repeated with subinterval sizes $h/2$ and $h/4$. This reduction by a factor of 2 can be repeated until the error estimate is smaller than the desired error.

Write a program to do such a calculation. It should have the parameters A, B, F, and E, where E is a real number that should exceed the error estimate. The program should use Program 19-1 to do the quadrature.

20

Continuous Simulation

■   ■   ■   ■   ■   ■   ■

Although continuous simulation finds most of its applications in engineering and science, many business and economic models use it as well. The central idea is that of values varying with time. For example, an economist might specify a model in which the increase in the gross national product is proportional to the total labor force and to the capital investment over the preceding year—that is, the rate of change in the gross national product is specified as a function of those other values. In a typical engineering problem, space flight, the rate of change in the velocity of the spacecraft might be proportional to the power generated by the propulsion system. The objective of the simulation is to determine how the system behaves over time, and frequently the ultimate objective is to select values for particular variables to achieve a particular goal.

To illustrate with a very simple example, suppose we are told that a rocket is generating enough thrust to accelerate it straight up by 1 meter/second (m/s) in every second—that is, in every second, its velocity increases by 1 m/s. How high will it be after 10 seconds, and how long will it take to reach a height of 1000 meters? As usual, the problem statement is incomplete: we need to know that the rocket is initially at rest or at some

TABLE 20-1 Distance Moved and Velocity of Rocket

Time (seconds)	Velocity (m/s) at End of Time	Total Vertical Distance Covered (meters)
0	0	0
1	1	0
2	2	1
3	3	3
4	4	6
5	5	10
6	6	15
. . .	. . .	. . .

prescribed velocity. If the rocket starts at rest, we can approximate the answer as follows: in the first second, the rocket is not moving, so it covers no distance; however, it does accelerate to 1 m/s. In the second second, it moves 1 meter and accelerates to 2 m/s. In the third second, it moves 2 meters and accelerates to 3 m/s, and so on. We can thus build a table showing the velocity and the total distance moved after each second. We get the result shown in Table 20-1.

The columns in this table can be computed very simply. The leftmost column is simply a count of the passage of time. The next column is started at zero and is increased by the acceleration (1) after each second. For this example, the value in this column is exactly the same as that in the time column. The last column is also set initially to zero and is increased by the velocity at the previous time after each second. It would be simple to solve the problems posed above: How high is it in 10 seconds? Just compute for 10 cycles. (The approximate answer would be 45 meters.) How long will it take to reach 1000 meters? Keep computing until the distance exceeds 1000 meters. (After 45 seconds, our approximation will be 990, after 46, it will be 1035.) As with the quadrature discussed in the previous chapter, this is only an approximation. We are assuming that the velocity is constant over a step of 1 second, as shown in Figure 20-1. The graph plots the height of the rocket versus time. The *slope* of the curve is the velocity of the rocket, and we see that in the approximation plotted, the slope is a constant for each 1-second interval, so the graph consists of a sequence of straight lines. In the true solution, the velocity of the rocket increases continuously, so we expect a graph like the one shown above the approximate solution in Figure 20-1.

In the quadrature examples in the previous chapter, we used two techniques to improve the accuracy of the solution. The first consisted of using smaller squares to estimate the area. Here, the equivalent is to use a shorter time period, or *step*, in which we assume a constant velocity. We

FIGURE 20-1   Height of rocket with time

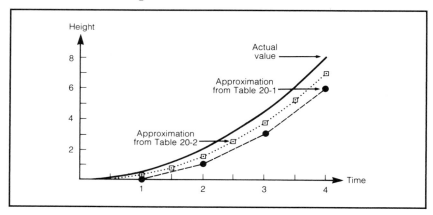

TABLE 20-2   Better Approximation to Height of Rocket

Time (seconds)	Velocity (m/s) at End of Time	Total Vertical Distance (meters)
0	0	0
0.5	0.5	0
1.0	1.0	0.25
1.5	1.5	0.75
2.0	2.0	1.5
2.5	2.5	2.5
3.0	3.0	3.75
3.5	3.5	5.25
4.0	4.0	7.0
. . .	. . .	. . .

could, for example, use a half-second. Now the calculation consists of computing first the velocity and then the height after each half-second step. Initially both are zero, as before. After 0.5 seconds, the velocity is 0.5 m/s, and the rocket has yet to move (in our approximation). After the next 0.5 seconds, the rocket is assumed to have risen at 0.5 m/s for 0.5 seconds, for a total rise of 0.25 meters. Further steps in this calculation are shown in Table 20-2. The calculation is exactly the same as in Table 20-1, provided that we remember that the elapsed time between rows is 0.5 seconds instead of a full second, so only half of the acceleration is added to the velocity and half of the velocity to the height. If the accuracy is insufficient, we could use a still smaller step.

The second approach to improving the accuracy discussed in the last chapter was to use a more accurate formula. That has its analogy here. For example, instead of assuming that the velocity is constant and equal to the value at the start of a step, we could assume that it was changing in some simple way, such as linearly with time. There are many numerical integration formulas based on assumptions such as these, but their study is not appropriate for this text. If the typical user has such a problem to solve, there are library programs in most computer installations that use some of these advanced methods. The important facts to remember are that problems of this sort can be solved approximately: the amount of accuracy that can be obtained is a function of the amount of computing time the user is willing to put into it. Even with the simple method discussed above (known as Euler's method), reasonable accuracy is possible if the step is made small enough. (The accuracy that is feasible for this method without excessive computer time is reasonable for fairly simple models, in which one or two digits of accuracy are sufficient. This method is not suitable for rocket trajectory computations, in which 10 to 15 digits of accuracy might be needed to ensure a safe landing on the moon.)

We will examine the details of this method with a further example, one that shows how this method can be applied to any type of problem in which we are told about the rate of change of values and want to track the behavior of the system as time proceeds.

Example 20.1
Rate of Chemical Reaction

A chemist has two substances, P and Q, in 1 liter of water. They are combining to form a third substance, R. The chemist knows that if the amounts of P and Q present in the water are p and q grams, respectively, then $2\alpha pq$ grams of R are formed during each second. It is also known that each gram of R formed requires 0.5 grams each of P and Q. Thus if at time t seconds there are p, q, and r grams, respectively, of P, Q, and R in the water, then at time $t + 1$ seconds there will be $p - \alpha pq$, $q - \alpha pq$, and $r + 2\alpha pq$ grams, respectively. However, there is also a second effect occurring: in each second, $2\beta r$ grams of R are breaking up into βr grams each of P and Q. Thus the change in 1 second is really

$$\text{amount of P increases by } \beta r - \alpha pq$$
$$\text{amount of Q increases by } \beta r - \alpha pq$$
$$\text{amount of R increases by } 2\alpha pq - 2\beta r$$

Thus if $p(t)$, $q(t)$, and $r(t)$ are the amounts of P, Q, and R at time t, we have the following formulas for the amounts at time $t + 1$:

$$p(t + 1) = p(t) + \beta r(t) - \alpha p(t)q(t)$$
$$q(t + 1) = q(t) + \beta r(t) - \alpha p(t)q(t)$$
$$r(t + 1) = r(t) - 2\beta r(t) + 2\alpha p(t)q(t)$$

This model can be simulated on the computer. A loop updates the amounts of p, q, and r once for each simulated second.

As before, we may not be happy with the accuracy of the approximation and would like to use a smaller time step. Suppose that we use a step of h seconds. Then our formulas for calculating future values of p, q, and r are

$$p(t + h) = p(t) + h\beta r(t) - h\alpha p(t)q(t)$$
$$q(t + h) = q(t) + h\beta r(t) - h\alpha p(t)q(t)$$
$$r(t + h) = r(t) - 2h\beta r(t) + 2h\alpha p(t)q(t)$$

Since we cannot calculate values of the variables for all values of the time t, we use the formulas above to calculate the values at a discrete set of time values 0, h, $2h$, $3h$, ... If the approximation to $p(t)$ at $t = nh$ is named p_n, and so on for the other variables, we get the relations

$$p_{n+1} = p_n + h\beta r_n - h\alpha p_n q_n$$
$$q_{n+1} = q_n + h\beta r_n - h\alpha p_n q_n$$
$$r_{n+1} = r_n - 2h\beta r_n + 2h\alpha p_n q_n$$

We hope that as h becomes smaller our model becomes more realistic, since we are assuming that the rate of production is constant for smaller and smaller intervals h. (We are also assuming that if z grams are being changed per second, then hz grams will be changed in h seconds.)

Fortunately it can be shown that as h gets smaller, the answers $p(t)$, $q(t)$, and $r(t)$ to such a model become more realistic. It can actually be shown that $p(t)$, $q(t)$, and $r(t)$ approach some continuous (smooth) functions $\hat{p}(t)$, $\hat{q}(t)$, and $\hat{r}(t)$ as h gets smaller, and that if $h\alpha$ and $h\beta$ are reasonably small, the numerical model described gives a very good approximation to these functions. We say that the numerical solutions *converge* to the continuous functions.*

Program 20-1 simulates the behavior of the chemical system by computing the values of p, q, and r every $1/m$ seconds for a total time of t_n

---

*In fact, they converge to the solution of the *differential equations*

$$\frac{dp}{dt} = \beta r - \alpha pq$$

$$\frac{dq}{dt} = \beta r - \alpha pq$$

$$\frac{dr}{dt} = -2\beta r + 2\alpha pq$$

The models described above can be used to solve such differential equations. Continuous simulation models usually give rise to differential equations that are solved by methods like these, but this subject is beyond the scope of a first course.

■ Program 20.1 Simulation of a simple chemical problem

```
CHEMISTRY: program
```
Concentrations of the substances `P`*,* `Q`*, and* `R` *are computed.*
Initial values, reaction rates, and the time interval can be specified.
```
real P = 0.0,Q = 0.0,R = 0.0,DP,ALPHA = 0.0,
BETA = 0.0
integer M = 1,TN = 1,I,J,CONTROL = 0
    do while CONTROL ≠ −1
        input CONTROL
```
A control number of 0 will give the user instructions
about what to do. Cases 0 through 4 are handled in a
`case` *statement. Other cases are ignored. A control*
number of −1 will terminate the loop after this pass.
```
        case (0,1,2,3,4,) of CONTROL
            0: output 'CONTROL VALUES ARE'
               output '−1 STOP            0 PRINT THIS TABLE'
               output '1 INITIAL VALUES  2 NEW ALPHA, BETA'
               ALPHA, BETA'
               output '3 NEW M,TN         4 SIMULATE'
            1: output 'INPUT INITIAL VALUES OF
               P,Q,R'
               input P,Q,R
            2: output 'INPUT ALPHA,BETA'
               input ALPHA,BETA
            3: output 'INPUT # STEPS/SECOND,TOTAL
               TIME'
               input M,TN
            4: output 'ALPHA = ',ALPHA,'BETA = ',
               BETA
               output 'SIMULATION WITH',M,'STEPS
               PER SECOND'
               output 'TIME','P','Q','R'
               output 0,P,Q,R
               do for I ← 1 to TN
```
Simulate for one second.
```
                   do for J ← 1 to M
```
Compute rate of change in 1/M
seconds.
```
                       DP ← (BETA*R − ALPHA*
                       P*Q)/FLOAT(M)
                       P ← P + DP
                       Q ← Q + DP
                       R ← R − 2.0*DP
                   enddo
               output I,P,Q,R
```

```
            │ enddo
         │ endcase
      │ enddo
   endprogram CHEMISTRY
```

seconds. This program is written for an interactive system: it outputs a request to the user whenever it needs more input. The user is given the option of specifying which variables should be changed from a previous simulation. This allows a person to sit at a terminal and experiment with the effects of various values for the parameters. The program is designed so that only values that change from the previous simulation need be specified. Consequently, initial values are specified for all variables that should be input by the user before the first simulation. This prevents the program from misbehaving if an input, such as t_n, is inadvertently left unspecified.

Program 20-1 *prompts* the user with a list of the items to be input. This method also provides a simple way of informing the user what control options may be specified. A *control number* indicates which variables the user wishes to change, but this arrangement is of no value unless the user can remember which number corresponds to which set of variables. It is a good idea in any interactive program to give the user a way to get a list of the available control options. Sometimes this can be done by testing for a special control input such as HELP. Since we do not want to use character strings in this program, we have chosen a control input of zero for this purpose. All the user has to remember is that an input of zero can be used to find out how to use the program.

PROBLEMS

1 An automatic speed control for an automobile has the following characteristics:

The velocity of the vehicle V is compared with the desired velocity VDES. The difference DIFF = VDES − V is used to adjust the accelerator position AP every second. The adjustment consists of an increase in AP by an amount equal to C*DIFF − D*AP, where C and D are coefficients to be determined by simulation. The automobile is assumed to obey a mathematical model in which its speed can be calculated each second from the equation

VNEW = V + AP − F*V

that is, if the speed at time T seconds is V and the accelerator position is AP, the speed at time T + 1 seconds is as given. The new accelerator position is given by

$$\mathtt{APNEW = AP + C*(VDES - V)}$$

Write a program to simulate the behavior of the automobile, assuming that the frictional force coefficient $\mathtt{F}$ is 0.5 and the desired velocity $\mathtt{VDES}$ is an input parameter. Try various values of the coefficient $\mathtt{C}$ between 0.1 and 0.8 to see what happens to the control system.

2 Some simulations require a mixture of continuous and discrete techniques. Consider a simulation of the temperature of a building controlled by an automatic heating system and subject to random comings and goings of people. A model of such a system has a continuous part, representing the temperature of the building and the rate of flow of heat into and out of it, and a discrete part, representing the turning on and off of the thermostat and the random arrivals and departures of people. Suppose we have the following model:

The temperature of the building at time $\mathtt{T + 1}$ is determined by the temperature of the building at time $\mathtt{T}$, the heat input, $\mathtt{H}$, from the heating system, the heat loss, $\mathtt{LOSS}$, through the walls, and the heat, $\mathtt{E}$, generated by other equipment as follows:

$$\mathtt{TEMPERATURE_{new} = TEMPERATURE + H - LOSS + E}$$

The heat input, $\mathtt{H}$, is either zero, if the heating system is off, or 0.63, if the system is on. The system is shut off at time $\mathtt{T + 1}$ if the temperature at time $\mathtt{T}$ is greater than $\mathtt{TEMPDESIRED + 1}$; it is turned on at time $\mathtt{T + 1}$ if the temperature at time $\mathtt{T}$ is less than $\mathtt{TEMPDESIRED - 1}$.

$\mathtt{LOSS}$ is given by $\mathtt{0.03*(TEMPERATURE - OUTSIDETEMP)}$

$\mathtt{E}$ is either 0 or 0.11, and changes from one value to the other as a person enters or leaves. For the model, $\mathtt{E}$ can be assumed to change from one value to the other with probability 0.1 during each unit of time—that is, if at time $\mathtt{T}$, $\mathtt{E}$ is 0.11, then at time $\mathtt{T + 1}$, $\mathtt{E}$ should be 0.11 with probability 0.9 and 0.0 with probability 0.1.

Write a program to simulate this system, assuming that $\mathtt{TEMP-DESIRED = 24}$ and $\mathtt{OUTSIDETEMP = -5}$. Find the *duty cycle* of the heating system—that is, the percentage of the time that it is on.

3 Consider the simple example used in Tables 20-1 and 20-2. Another type of approximation that could be used is to assume that the velocity is constant in each step, but has a value equal to the average of the values at the beginning and end of the step. Thus, in the first step of Table 20-1, the average value of the velocity would be 0.5 m/s. Hence, the distance covered would be 0.5 meters. Use this approximation with both the 1-second step (Table 20-1) and the half-second step (Table

20-2) and show that they give the same results. In fact, because the acceleration is constant, this method gives the correct answer for any step size. (Unfortunately, as soon as the acceleration is nonconstant, this property disappears.) Use this answer to calculate the errors in Tables 20-1 and 20-2. What is the relationship between them? Why do you think they have this relationship?

Index

D

Data structure, 49ff
Definite integral, 223
Degree, 72
Deque, 44ff
Derivative, 113
Descendant, 52
Deterministic, 198
Diagonal array, 100
    dominance, 120
Differential equation, 236
Digraph. *See* Directed graph
Directed acyclic graph (DAG), 186
Directed graph, 145, 186
Directed list, 144
Divide and conquer, 16
Divisor, greatest common, 8
Dyadic operation, 160

E

Elimination, 99
Enumeration, 8, 17, 148
Equations
    linear, 95ff
    nonlinear, 91
    sparse, 104
Error
    measurement, 80
    rounding, 126ff
    truncation, 127, 132ff
Event, 204
Exit loop, 9
Exp, 65
Exponentiation, 4

F

False position method, 108
First-in-first-out (FIFO) list, 45
Free list, 41
Full pivoting, 141
Function, 10
    periodic, 66
Functions, 63ff

G

Gauss elimination, 99
Gauss-Seidel method, 121
General purpose system simulation
    (GPSS), 205
Graph, 145ff
    acyclic, 186

connected, 145
directed, 145, 186
planar, 146
undirected, 145
Greatest common divisor (GCD), 8

H

Head, queue, 44
Hierarchy, 176

I

Identifier, 4
Ill-conditioned, 133
Index, 23
Infix notation, 164
Insertion sort, 28–29
Integral, 223
Interarrival time, 208
Interpolation, 74
    linear, 75
Iterate, 9, 119
Iteration, 9, 17
Iterative method, 9

J

Jacobi method, 120

K

Key, 8

L

Last-in-first-out (LIFO) list, 45
Law of large numbers, 199
Least squares, 82
Leave, 51
Linear interpolation, 75
Linear problems, 92
Linearization, 122
Linked list, 37
List, 34ff, 143
    chained, 37, 212
    FIFO, 45
    free, 41
    LIFO, 45
    linked, 37
    ordered, 41
    tree, 52
Log, 65
Loop, 8

M

Mean, 130
Median, 30
Merge, 43
  sort, 30, 43ff
    binary, 43ff
Minimax, 87
Model, 204
Monadic operation, 161
Monotonic, 14

N

Newton method, 9, 112, 124
Node, 51, 143
Numerical quadrature, 219ff

O

Offspring, 51
  left, 52
  right, 52
One-way list, 143
Operand, 164–165
Operator, 164–165
Ordered list, 41
  tree, 52
Orthogonal polynomials, 85

P

Partial ordering, 185
  pivoting, 141
Partition, 30–31
Periodic, 66
Piecewise-linear, 78
Pivot, 97
Pivoting, full, 141
  partial, 141
Pointer, 34ff
Polish notation, 160
  postfix, 166
  prefix, 164
Polynomial, 71–72
  orthogonal, 85
Pop, 45
Power series, 65
Precedence, 177
Prefix notation, 164
Probabilistic, 200
'Probability, 199
Problem-oriented language, 205
Prompt, 238
Push, 45

Q

Quadrature, 217, 219ff
  adaptive, 230
Queue, 44ff
Quicksort, 30–32

R

RANDOM, 198
Record, 7, 8
Recursion, 61
Refine, 24
Regula falsi method, 108
Residual, 121
Root, 11, 51
Rounding, 7
Rounding error, 126ff

S

Search, 7
  binary, 13–16, 50
  sequential, 8
Secant method, 111
Selection sort, 23–25
Sequential method, 23
  search, 8
Series, 24
  alternating, 68
  geometric, 6
  power, 65
Shortest path problem, 152
Simpson's rule, 227ff
Simulate, 13
Simulated clock, 206
Simulation verification, 205
Sin, 65
Slope, 233
Sort
  binary, 29–32
  bubble, 26–28
  insertion, 28–29
  merge, 30
  selection, 23–25
Sparse equations, 104
Sparse matrix, 156ff
Spline, 78
Square root, 9
Stack, 44ff, 59
  overflow, 45
  top, 44
  underflow, 45
Step, integration, 233